DATE DUE

TOAD OF TOAD HALL

TOAD OF
TOAD HALL

A Play from Kenneth Grahame's Book

A. A. MILNE

CHARLES SCRIBNER'S SONS
New York

SCENES

PROLOGUE AND ACT I.
Down by the Willows.

ACT II.

ACT III.

ACT IV.

EPILOGUE.
The Wind in the Willows.

CHARACTERS

NURSE.

MARIGOLD.

THE MOLE.

THE WATER-RAT.

MR. BADGER.

TOAD.

ALFRED.

CHIEF WEASEL.

CHIEF STOAT.

CHIEF FERRET.

FIRST FIELD MOUSE.

SECOND FIELD MOUSE.

USHER.

POLICEMAN.

JUDGE.

PHOEBE.

WASHERWOMAN.

MAMA RABBIT.

HAROLD RABBIT.

LUCY RABBIT.

FOX.

BARGE-WOMAN.

A BRAVE YOUNG WEASEL (HENRY).

A FOOLISH FERRET (JAMES).

Barge-horse, Squirrels, Rabbits, Ferrets, Weasels, Stoats, Field Mice, Turkey, Duck, Back Legs of Alfred, etc., etc.

INTRODUCTION

THERE are familiarities which we will allow only ourselves to take. Your hands and my hands are no cleaner than anybody else's hands, yet the sort of well-thumbed bread-and-butter which we prefer is that on which we have placed our own thumbs. It may be that to turn Mr. Kenneth Grahame into a play is to leave unattractive finger marks all over him, but I love his books so much that I cannot bear to think of anybody else disfiguring them. That is why I accepted a suggestion, which I should have refused in the case of any other book as too difficult for me, that I should dramatize *The Wind in the Willows*.

There are two well-known ways in which to make a play out of a book. You may insist on being faithful to the author, which means that the scene in the airplane on page 673 must be got in somehow, however impossible dramatically; or with somebody else's idea in your pocket, you may insist on being faithful to yourself, which means that by the middle of Act III everybody will realize how right the original author was to have made a book of it. There may be a third way, in which case I have tried to follow it. If, as is more likely, there isn't, then I have not made a play of *The Wind in the Willows*. But I have, I hope, made some sort of entertainment, with enough of Kenneth Grahame in it to appease his many admirers, and enough of me in it to justify my name upon the title-page.

Of course I have left out all the best parts of the book; and for that, if he has any knowledge of the theater, Mr. Grahame will thank me. With a Rat and Mole from the Green

Room Club, a Baby Otter from Conti, a Pan from Clarkson's, and a wind (off) whispering in the reeds of Harker, we are not going to add any fresh thrill to the thrill which the loveliness of *The Piper at the Gates of Dawn* has already given its readers. Whether there is, indeed, any way of putting these animals on the stage must be left to managers, professional and amateur, to find out. But it seemed clear to me that Rat and Toad, Mole and Badger could only face the footlights with hope of success if they were content to amuse their audiences. There are both beauty and comedy in the book, but the beauty must be left to blossom there, for I, anyhow, shall not attempt to transplant it.

But can one transplant even the comedy? Perhaps it has happened to you, as it has certainly happened to me, that you have tried to explain a fantastic idea to an entirely matter-of-fact person. "But they don't," he says, and "You can't," and "I don't see why, just because," and "Even if you assume that," and "I thought you said just now that he hadn't." By this time you have thrown the ink-pot at him, with enough accuracy, let us hope, to save you from his ultimatum, which is this: "However fantastic your assumption, you must work it out logically," that is to say, realistically.

To such a mind *The Wind in the Willows* makes no appeal, for it is not worked out logically. In reading the book it is necessary to think of Mole, for instance, sometimes as an actual mole, sometimes as such a mole in human clothes, sometimes as a mole grown to human size, sometimes as walking on two legs, sometimes on four. He is a mole, he isn't a mole. What is he? I don't know. And, not being a matter-of-fact person, I don't mind. At least, I do know, and still I don't mind. He is a fairy, like so many immortal characters in fiction; and, as a fairy, he can do, or be, anything.

But the stage has no place for fairies. There is a horrid

realism about the theater, from which, however hard we try, we can never quite escape. Once we put Mole and his friends on the boards we have to be definite about them. What do they look like?

To answer this here is difficult. To say at rehearsal what they do not look like will be easy. Vaguely I see them made up on the lines of the Cat in *The Blue Bird* and the Hen Pheasant in *Chantecler*. As regards their relative sizes, Toad should be short and fat, Badger tall and elderly, Rat and Mole young and slender. Indeed Mole might well be played by some boyish young actress. The "humans," Judge, Policeman, Usher and the rest, should be as fantastic as possible, with a hint of the animal world about them. Only Phoebe must keep her own pretty face, but even she must be no mortal. I see her in a ballet skirt or something entirely unsuitable to a gaoler's daughter, pirouetting absurdly about the prison.

But no doubt the producer will see them all differently. If he is an amateur, I shall congratulate him on his enterprise and wish him luck; if he is a professional, I shall be there to watch him, and, no doubt, to tell him enthusiastically how much better his ideas are than mine.

A. A. M.

TOAD OF TOAD HALL

ACT I

DOWN BY THE WILLOWS

Scene. *The River Bank. A warm morning in spring.*
nurse *was knitting a sock, but seems to have fallen
asleep over it. This leaves* marigold *(who is twelve)
to amuse herself. She is lying on her front, and talking down the telephone. At least she has the trumpet
of one daffodil to her ear, and of another to her mouth,
and has apparently just got on to the Exchange.*

MARIGOLD

Hallo, is that the Exchange? I want River Bank 1001. . . .
Hallo, is that the Water Rat's house? . . . Oh, I beg your
pardon. They've given me the wrong number. . . . Oh,
Exchange, you've given me the wrong number. I wanted
Mr. Rat's house and you've given me Mr. Badger's. (*To
herself*) Sorry you've been tr-r-roubled. . . . Hallo, is that
the Water Rat's house? Is that Mr. Rat speaking? Good
morning, Mr. Rat, this is Marigold speaking. . . . Yes, isn't
it a delightful day? . . . Yes. Well, almost alone. Nurse is
here, but she's asleep. How's Mr. Mole? . . . Oh, haven't
you seen him? I expect he's very busy spring cleaning. You
see, when your house is all basement, there's such a lot of
spring cleaning to be done. . . . Yes, I prefer a riverside

3

residence too. . . . May I really come one day? How lovely.
. . . No, not tomorrow, I'm having tea with Mr. Toad.
. . . Yes, conceited, but so nice. . . . I saw Mr. Otter just
now, just before I rang you up. . . . No, I don't know him
very well, but I think he's sweet. . . . Will you really? And
if Mr. Mole—

NURSE (*who was not asleep*)
Well, I declare, Miss Marigold, you do think of funny
things.

MARIGOLD (*hurriedly*)
Oh, Nurse is awake. Good-bye. (*She puts down the telephone and says sternly*) Have you been overhearing, Nurse?

NURSE (*nodding*)
And wondering at you, dearie. Who ever heard the like?

MARIGOLD
It's very bad manners to overhear a perfectly private telephone conversation.

NURSE
Couldn't help it, dearie, you're that funny—with your Mr.
Rat and Mr. Toad and all, just as if they were yooman
beings.

MARIGOLD
Well, but so they are.

NURSE (*surprised at this*)
Yooman beings?

MARIGOLD

Yes. I mean they are as human to themselves as—as we are to us.

NURSE (*after a gallant effort*)

No, it's no good, dearie, I can't follow it.

MARIGOLD

I mean, they must seem quite big and grown up and human to each other, and if we lived in their world, then they would seem big and grown up to us, just like real people.

NURSE

Now, fancy that!

MARIGOLD

Mr. Toad, he's all puffed out and conceited, but very nice, you know, and very sorry afterwards for talking so much about himself. And Mr. Rat's a dear; that's him I was talking to just now. He's very quick and clever and helpful, and his little sharp eyes are always looking out so as to see that he doesn't hurt people's feelings. And Mr. Mole, I'm not sure about him. You see, he lives underground a good deal and doesn't go out into society much, so I should think he'd be rather simple and not liking to talk about himself, and just saying "Yes" and "No," and waiting to be asked before he has a second cup. And then Mr. Badger. Of course he's gray and much older than the others, and very fatherly, and sleeps a good deal with a handkerchief over his face, and says "Now, now, now," and "Well, well, well" when he's woken up. And Mr. Otter—

NURSE

Well, well, well, fancy that now! Why, you might almost have seen them at it, the way you talk.

MARIGOLD

I have.

NURSE

Never!

MARIGOLD

Yes. One morning. I came out here early, oh, ever so early. Nobody was up; you weren't up, and the birds weren't up and even the sun wasn't up. And everything was so still that there was no sound in all the world, except just the wind in the willows, whispering ever so gently.

NURSE (*professionally*)

What your poor mother would have said. (*Eagerly*) Well, and what happened?

MARIGOLD

I don't know. I sat there and waited for everything to wake up, and then by and by I heard something, music, very thin and clear and far off. And then, well then there was the sun, and it was daylight, and it seemed as if I had just woken up myself. But it was all different. Something had happened. I didn't know what, but I seemed to understand more than I did before—to have been *with* them.

NURSE

Mr. Toad and Mr. Mole and all them?

MARIGOLD

Yes. I've never really seen them since. I pretend to talk to them just as if they were really there, but— (*With sudden excitement*) Wouldn't it be lovely if they suddenly came out and began to talk—Mole from under the ground there, and the Water Rat from his hole in the bank, and the old Badger from the dead leaves in the ditch, and Mr. Toad—

NURSE

I should be that frightened, if they were all big.

MARIGOLD

Oh no, you wouldn't, because they wouldn't know we were here. We should just listen to them without their knowing anything about it. (*She calls out*) Mr. Mole! Mr. Rat! Mr. Toad! Oh, Nurse, wouldn't it be lovely?

NURSE

Oo, I can hear something! Listen!

MARIGOLD

That's the music again. Quick! Hide!

(*It is dark suddenly, and we hear music, very thin and clear and far off: "the horns of Elfland faintly blowing." Gradually it grows light again. There is no* NURSE, *no* MARIGOLD *now. But near where* MARIGOLD *was lying there is a curious upheaval going on. The earth moves and humps up and falls back again. Somebody is at work underneath. We hear breathings and mutterings. In a little while we can distinguish words. It is our old friend* MOLE.)

MOLE (*as he comes laboriously into the daylight*)
Scrape and scratch and scrabble and scrooge, scrooge and scrabble and scrape and scratch. Up we go, up we go. . . . Pop! (*He stands up and brushes himself.*) Ah! (*He takes a deep breath of daylight.*) This is fine. This is better than whitewash. Hang spring cleaning! (*He walks about, making ecstatic noises to himself.*) Oh, what a day. Oh my, oh my, oh my. Blow spring cleaning! (*He rubs his eyes with his paw.*) Is that a river? Oh my, oh my. Bother spring cleaning!

(*The river has hollowed out a little bay here so that* NURSE *and* MARIGOLD, *from where they are sitting in Box B, can see their own side of the bank, where it bends round in a curve; and they can see* RAT'S *front door and they can see bright eyes and a sharp friendly face with whiskers as the* WATER RAT *comes out of it.*)

RAT
Hallo, Mole.

MOLE
Hallo, Rat.

RAT
Don't seem to have seen you about before.

MOLE (*shyly*)
I—I don't go out much, as a rule.

RAT (*cheerily*)

Prefer home life? *I* know. Very good thing too in its way.

MOLE

Yes, you see, I— This is a river, isn't it?

RAT

The River.

MOLE (*simply*)

I've never seen a river before.

RAT (*staggered*)

Never seen a— You never— Well, I— What have you been doing then?

MOLE

Is it as nice as that?

RAT

Nice? My dear young friend, believe me, it's the *only* thing. There is nothing, absolutely nothing, half so much worth doing as simply messing about by a river. (*Dreamily*) Simply messing, messing about by a river, or in a river or on a river. It doesn't matter which.

MOLE

But what do you *do?*

RAT

Nothing. Just mess about. That's the charm of it. You're

always busy, and yet you never do anything in particular; and when you've done it, there's always something else to do, and you can do it if you like, but you'd much better not. . . . And so you've never even seen a river before? Well, well.

MOLE

Never. And you actually live by it. What a jolly life it sounds.

RAT

By it and with it and on it and in it. It's brother and sister to me, and aunts and company, and food and drink and naturally, washing. It's my world and I don't want any other.

MOLE

Isn't it a bit dull at times? Just you and the river and no one else to pass a word with?

RAT

No one else to—no one— Oh well, I mustn't be hard on you. You're new to it. But believe me, my dear young friend, the River Bank is so crowded nowadays that many people are moving away altogether: otters, kingfishers, dabchicks, moorhens. No one else to—oh, my dear young friend.

MOLE (*timidly*)

I am afraid you must think me very ignorant.

RAT (*kindly*)

Not at all. Naturally, not being used to it. Look here, what are you doing today?

MOLE (*hesitatingly*)

I—I was spring cleaning.

RAT

On a day like this?

MOLE

That's just it. Sometimes I seem to hear a voice within me say "Whitewash," and then another voice says "Hang white-wash!" (*Slowly*) And I don't know quite which of the— I don't quite know—I don't qui— Oh, hang whitewash!

RAT (*patting him encouragingly*)

That's the spirit. Well, what I was about to suggest was a trifle of lunch on the bank here, and then I'd take you round and introduce you to a few of my friends. Does that appeal to you at all?

MOLE (*ecstatically*)

Does it appeal to me? Does it? Oh my, oh my, oh my.

RAT (*soothingly*)

There, there. You don't want to get too excited. It's only just a trifle of lunch: cold tongue, cold ham, cold chicken, salad, french rolls, cress sandwiches, hard-boiled eggs, bloater paste, tinned peaches, meringues, ginger beer, lemonade, milk chocolate, oranges. Nothing special, only just—

MOLE (*faintly*)

Stop, stop. Oh my, oh my. Oh, what a day!

RAT

That's all right. You'll feel better soon. Now just you wait here, don't go falling into the river or anything like that, and I'll be back in two minutes with the luncheon basket.

MOLE (*wiping away the tears*)

Oh, Mr. Rat, my generous friend, I—I—words fail me for the moment—I— (*He holds out his hand.*) Your kindness— that expression, if I caught it correctly, "luncheon basket" —a comparative stranger like myself—did I hear you say "bloater paste?" You—I— (*He opens his eyes and finds that* RAT *has gone.*) Oh! (*He walks over to a bank of dead leaves and sits down on it.*) Oh, what a day!

> (*It is indeed a day. For suddenly the leaves begin to move beneath him, and* MOLE *rises and falls with the motion of a small boat on a choppy sea. A final up-heaval dislodges him altogether and leaves scatter and disclose the recumbent form of* MR. BADGER. *Slowly he humps himself into a sitting position and addresses the astonished* MOLE.)

BADGER (*gruffly*)

Now the very next time this happens I shall be exceedingly angry. I have had to speak about it before and I don't want to speak about it again. But I will not have people sitting down on me just as if I were part of the landscape. Now who is it this time? Speak up.

MOLE

Oh, please, Mr. Badger, it's only me.

BADGER

Well, if it's only you, that makes a difference. I don't want
to be hard on you. But I put it to you that when an animal
is being particularly busy underneath a few leaves, thinking
very deeply about things, giving himself up to very serious
reflection, he does not want to be disturbed. And it is disturbing, my little fellow, to have somebody sitting down
carelessly on your person, and stretching his legs in an in-
dependent sort of way, and—

RAT (*emerging with the lunch*)

Here, Mole, give us a hand with this basket. Hallo! Why,
it's Mr. Badger.

BADGER

Ah, Ratty, my dear little man, delighted to see you. I was
just telling this little fellow—

RAT

By the way, let me introduce you. My friend, Mr. Mole.

BADGER

Don't mention it. Any friend of yours, Ratty—

MOLE (*timidly*)

How do you do, Mr. Badger? I am very proud to meet you.
I'm sure I'm extremely sorry—

BADGER

That's all right, that's all right. Any friend of Ratty's may sit down where he likes and when he likes, or I'll know the reason why. Well, and what are you two little fellows doing?

RAT

Just having a trifle of lunch. Stay and join us, won't you?

MOLE (*shyly*)

Oh do, Mr. Badger. It's a picnic. (*He helps* RAT *up with the basket.*)

BADGER

H'm. Picnics aren't much in my line. Got company coming?

RAT

Only Mole and myself. Unless Toad happens along.

MOLE (*in an ecstatic whisper*)

There's cold tongue, cold chicken, salad, french rolls, cress sandwiches, hard-boiled eggs—

BADGER

Well, if you're sure there's no company. You know, Ratty, I never did like society. (*He sits down heavily on the basket, much to* MOLE's *disappointment, who was hoping to get to work at once.*)

RAT

Can't say I see much in it myself.

BADGER

Sensible animal. And what about your friend Mr. Mole?

MOLE

Oh, I live a very quiet life, Mr. Badger. A field mouse or two drops in from time to time, perhaps half a dozen of them will come carol singing at Christmas, but beyond that I hardly see anybody.

BADGER

That's right. Ratty, your little friend promises well.

RAT

Yes, but you're sitting on the lunch, and we can't—

BADGER (*taking no notice*)

He has the right ideas. (*Solemnly*) How different from *one* whom we could mention.

RAT

Oh, Toad? Toady's all right.

BADGER (*shaking his head sadly*)

Ah me.

MOLE

I have heard of the great Mr. Toad. He's very rich, isn't he?

RAT

Richest animal in these parts, and got one of the nicest houses, though we don't admit as much to Toady. Tudor residence: mullioned windows, bath, hot and cold, and every modern convenience, including carriage sweep. Entertains a lot. Always glad to see you night or day. A good fellow, Toady.

BADGER

Ah me!

MOLE

He must indeed be a very nice animal.

RAT

So simple, so good-natured, so affectionate. Perhaps he's not very clever, we can't all be geniuses; and it may be that he is both boastful and conceited. But he has some great qualities has Toady.

MOLE

It would be a privilege to make his acquaintance.

RAT

Oh, you'll see him all right. He's sure to be along soon.

BADGER

And when you see him, my little friend, take warning by him. Society has been his undoing.

RAT

Well, I wouldn't say that. I—

BADGER

If it were not for the desire to shine before his acquaintances, what a much more dependable animal Toad would be. I knew his father. I knew his grandfather. I knew his uncle, the Archdeacon. Ah me.

RAT

Cheer up, old Badger. We'll take him in hand one day and make a better animal of him.

BADGER

Indeed we must. It is a duty I owe to his father. And now that the year is really beginning, and the nights are shorter, and halfway through them one rouses and feels fidgety, and wanting to be up and doing by sunrise, if not before, you know—

RAT

I know.

BADGER

Well then, now we—you and me and our friend the Mole here, we'll take him in hand and make a better animal of him. That is, if we have any more of his nonsense.

RAT (*nodding*)

That's right, Badger. But he's a good fellow, Toady. Doesn't mean any harm, you know. Just his way.

MOLE

What is his way?

BADGER

You tell him, Rat.

RAT

Crazes. He always has crazes. First it's for sailing, and then it's for punting, and then it's for astronomy, and then it's for carriage horses; and whatever it is, he always has the most expensive, and lots of 'em, and knows all about it, or thinks he does, and— Just get up a moment, Badger, you're sitting on the basket.

BADGER (*not moving*)

I knew his father. I knew his uncle the—

RAT

Whatever it is, he must have the best. And then in a week he's forgotten about it and started something else.

BADGER

Society. That's what's undone him. The craving to shine. (*Solemnly to* MOLE) Very sad, my young friend, very sad. I knew his grandfather.

MOLE (*helpfully*)

Dear, dear.

BADGER

What his poor father would have said.

TOAD (*off*)

Hallo!

RAT (*cheerily*)

Hallo, Toady. (*He waves a paw.*) I thought he'd come along soon. You see, he likes company.

BADGER (*sadly*)

Ah me.

(TOAD *comes in boisterously, as full of himself as usual.*)

TOAD

Hallo, you fellows. This is splendid. Hallo, old Badger. Dear old Ratty. (*He shakes him warmly by the paw.*) Hallo! (*He seizes* MOLE's *paw and works it up and down.*) And dear old Badger. (*He passes on to* BADGER.) How are you?

BADGER

So-so.

TOAD

Splendid, splendid.

RAT

My friend, Mr. Mole.

TOAD (*going back enthusiastically to* MOLE)

How are you? (*He shakes his paw vigorously.*) Splendid, eh? That's good. And old Ratty. And Badger.

BADGER

We were talking about you, my young friend.

TOAD (*spreading himself with delight*)

Ah well, the penalty of fame. Eh, Ratty? One gets talked about. One is discussed. One is a topic of conversation. One is speculated about. There it is. One can't help it. Well, Ratty old man, and how are you?

RAT

I'm all right. We were just going to have a trifle of lunch. You'd better join us. (*Pulling at the basket again*) I say, Badger, old man—

TOAD

No, no, you all come up to my house. Come up to Toad Hall. I'll give you lunch, the finest lunch you ever had.

MOLE (*unable to imagine anything superior to* RAT's *effort*)

But there's cold tongue, cold ham, cold chicken, salad, french rolls, cress sandwiches, hard-boiled—

TOAD

Pooh! Wait till you've seen mine. Ratty knows. Eh, Ratty? They're quite famous, been referred to in books. "Another select little luncheon party at Toad Hall." That sort of thing.

MOLE (*awed*)

Oh! (*He looks anxiously at* RAT, *to whom, after all, he is engaged for lunch.*)

RAT

Now, now, Toad.

BADGER

Well, I'll be moving. (*He rises slowly.*)

RAT (*getting to the basket at last*)

Thanks, old chap.

TOAD

That's right. We'll all be moving. (*To* MOLE) It's only a step to Toad Hall. Jacobean residence with bits of Tudor. Finest house on the river. You'll like it.

MOLE (*eagerly*)

I'm sure I shall.

BADGER (*to* MOLE)

Good-bye, my young friend. We shall meet again. And before very long, if I'm not mistaken. Good-bye, Ratty.

RAT

Sure you won't stay to lunch?

TOAD

But you are coming to lunch with me, old Badger.

BADGER (*severely*)

Nobody is coming to lunch with you, Toad. Many a time I have lunched at Toad Hall with your father, an animal of few words, but of what an intellect! Ah me. How different from—but I will not go into that now. Hour after hour, when lunch was cleared away, we would sit there, meditating. I knew your grandfather, worthy animal that he was. Many a time have I lunched with him at Toad Hall. Little did he think, as we sat there reflecting, that one day—but I shall refer to that later. Good-bye, my unhappy young friend. (*He goes out heavily.*)

MOLE (*anxiously*)

Isn't Mr. Badger feeling very well?

TOAD (*recovering himself*)

Poor old Badger, he gets that way sometimes. No fire, no spirit. No, what's the word, *élan*. Well, well, we can't all have it. Hallo, Ratty, where are you off to?

RAT (*going for it*)

The corkscrew.

TOAD (*not moving*)

Now, let me fetch it. (*To* MOLE) Tell you what, you must come and stay with me. Let me put you up at Toad Hall.

MOLE

It's very kind of you, but—

TOAD

That's all right. Plenty of room at Toad Hall. Open house for my friends. Always glad to see them. Now what have we got for lunch? (*He assumes the position of host.*) Try one of these sandwiches. (*As* RAT *emerges with the corkscrew*) Come along, Ratty, try one of these sandwiches. Got the corkscrew? Good. (*To* MOLE) Let me open you one of these bottles. Sit down, Ratty; make yourself comfortable.

RAT (*quietly to* MOLE)

Got everything you want?

MOLE

Yes, thank you.

RAT

That's right. Well, Toady, and what have you been doing lately? Boating? Haven't seen you on the river this last day or two.

TOAD

The river! Boating! Bah! Silly boyish amusement. I've given that up long ago. Sheer waste of time. No, I've discovered the real thing, the only genuine occupation. I propose to devote the remainder of my life to it. To think of the wasted years that lie behind me, squandered in trivialities.

RAT

What's that? Help yourself, Mole.

TOAD

Aha, what is it? Come to Toad Hall and you shall see.

MOLE

Oh, do let's.

RAT

All right, we'll drop in one afternoon.

TOAD

Drop in? One afternoon? Nonsense! You're coming to stay. Always welcome, that's my motto. I've had it picked out in green on the front door mat. "Always welcome. A home from home." (*To* MOLE) You'd like to come, wouldn't you?

RAT

Sorry, but Mole is staying with me.

TOAD

Now, you dear good old Ratty, don't begin talking in that stiff and sniffy sort of way, because you know you've got to come. And don't argue; it's the one thing I can't stand. You surely don't mean to stick to your dull fusty old river all your life and just live in a hole in the bank? Come and stay with me and I'll show you the world.

RAT

I don't want to see the world. And I am going to stick to my old river and live in a hole, just as I've always done. And I'm going to teach Mole all about the river, aren't I, Mole? And Mole is going to stick to me and do as I do, aren't you, Mole?

MOLE (*loyally*)

Of course I am. I'll always stick to you, Rat. (*Wistfully*) All the same, it sounds as though it might have been—well, rather fun at Toad Hall.

TOAD

Fun? Wait till you see what I've got. I've got the finest— well, wait till you see it. Pass the sandwiches, Mole, there's a good fellow. (*To* RAT) Seen any of the Wild Wooders lately?

RAT

No.

MOLE

Who are the Wild Wooders?

RAT (*pointing across the river*)

They live over there in the Wild Wood. We don't go there very much, we River Bankers.

MOLE

Aren't they, aren't they very nice people in there?

TOAD

They daren't show their noses round Toad Hall, that they daren't. I'd soon send them packing.

RAT

The squirrels are all right. And the rabbits, of course. And then there's Badger. Dear old Badger. Nobody interferes with him. They'd better not.

TOAD

And nobody wouldn't interfere with me neither, if I lived there.

MOLE

Why, who should?

RAT

Well, of course there are others. Weasels and stoats and ferrets, and so on. They're all right in a way. I'm very good friends with them.

TOAD

So am I.

RAT

Pass the time of day when we meet and all that. But they break out sometimes, there's no denying it, and then—well, you really can't trust them, and that's a fact. And if they don't like you, they—well, they show it.

TOAD

I wouldn't ask them to Toad Hall, not if they sat up and begged me to. I'm not afraid of them; I just don't like them. They've got no manners, no *finesse*, if you understand me. Some people are like that, of course. It isn't their fault. You either have *finesse*, or you haven't. That's how I look at it. Pass the meringues, Mole, there's a good fellow. (*But* MOLE *is staring beyond* TOAD *at something strange which is approaching, a gaily painted caravan drawn by an old gray horse.*)

RAT

What is it, Mole?

MOLE

Whatever's that? (*They all turn.*)

ALFRED (*the horse*)

Oh, there you are. I've been looking for you everywhere.

TOAD (*excitedly*)

Now isn't this lucky? Just at the psycho—psycho—what's the word?

ALFRED (*hopefully*)

Encyclopedia. That is, if you ask me.

TOAD

I didn't ask you. Ratty, you know the word.

ALFRED

Introduce me to your friends, won't you? I do get so frightfully left out of it.

TOAD

My friends Mr. Rat and Mr. Mole. This is Alfred.

ALFRED

Pleased to meet you. If you're coming my way, you must let me take you. Only I do like a little conversation. (*To* TOAD) Encyclopedia, that was the word you wanted.

RAT (*sadly*)

So this is the latest?

TOAD (*eagerly*)

Absolutely the very latest. There isn't a more beautiful one, a more compact one, a more—what's the word?

ALFRED

Heavy.

TOAD

A more up-to-date one, a more—

RAT

So this is the latest craze! I understand. Boating is played out. He's tired of it, and done with it.

ALFRED

Don't blame me. I wasn't consulted about this at all; but if I had been, I should have said boats. Stick to boats.

TOAD

My dear old Ratty, you don't understand. Boating—well, a pleasant amusement for the young. I say nothing against it. But there's real life for you (*He waves a paw at the van.*) in that little cart. The open road, the dusty highway, the heath, the common, the hedgerows, the rolling downs!

ALFRED

And the ups. However, nobody consults me. Nobody minds what I think.

TOAD (*warming to it*)

Camps, villages, towns, cities! Here today, up and off to somewhere else tomorrow. Travel, change, interest, excitement. The whole world before you, and a horizon that's always changing.

MOLE (*ecstatically*)

Oh my! Oh my!

TOAD

And mind, this is the very finest cart of the sort that was ever built, without any exception. Come inside and look at the arrangements, Mole. Planned 'em all myself, I did.

MOLE (*timidly to* RAT)

We could just look inside, couldn't we? It wouldn't— wouldn't mean anything.

ALFRED (*airily*)
Nothing. Nothing.

RAT (*reluctantly*)
Oh well, we may as well look at it now we are here. (*Sadly*)
Oh, Toady!

TOAD (*leading the way*)
All complete! You see: biscuits, potted lobster, sardines,
everything you can possibly want. Soda water here, baccy
there. (*He shows them into the van and then his voice dies
away.*)

ALFRED (*to anybody who is listening*)
That's right. Go inside and enjoy yourselves. Talk to each
other, tell each other little stories, but don't ask me to join
in the conversation. Encyclopedia, that was the word he
wanted. I could have told him.

TOAD (*emerging*)
Bacon, jam, cards, dominoes. You'll find that nothing whatever has been forgotten.

ALFRED (*with feeling*)
I've noticed it.

TOAD
Well, what do you think of it, Mole?

MOLE
It's lovely!

TOAD

Glad you like it. What about starting this afternoon?

RAT (*slowly*)

I beg your pardon. Did I overhear you say something about "starting"?

ALFRED

Starting, that's what he said. I'm not even consulted.

TOAD

Come on, we'll just put the rest of the lunch inside. Come on, Mole, give us a hand.

MOLE (*torn between the two of them*)

Oh, Ratty!

TOAD

Come on, Ratty, old fellow. This is the real life for a gentleman. Talk about your old river! (*He begins packing up the lunch.*)

RAT

I don't talk about my river. You know I don't, Toad. But I think it. I think about it all the time.

MOLE (*squeezing* RAT's *paw*)

I'll do whatever you like, Ratty. We won't go. I want to stay with you. And—learn about your river.

RAT

No, no, we'd better see it out now. It wouldn't be safe for

him to go off by himself. It won't take long. His crazes never do.

ALFRED

When *I* was young it was considered bad manners to whisper and leave people out of conversations. (*In a loud conversational voice*) My own view, since asked, of the climatic conditions, is that the present anti-cyclonic disturbance in the—

TOAD

Here, give us a hand, Mole. . . . That's right. . . . All aboard? Here, we're forgetting the corkscrew. Will you get it? (MOLE *trots back for it.*) Don't bother. I'll—oh, you've got it. Good. Now then, are we all ready?

ALFRED

No.

TOAD

You get up there, Mole. (MOLE *sits on the shaft on one side of the caravan.*) You on the other side, Ratty? Or would you rather— (RAT *goes to the horse's head.*) Oh, are you going to lead him? I will, if you like. Sure you don't mind? Right, then I'll get up here. Now then, right away!

(*They start off.*)

ALFRED (*to* RAT)

You mark my words. No good will come of this. But don't blame me. That's all. Don't blame me afterwards. Psychological, that was the word he wanted. Not encyclopedia. I thought it seemed funny somehow. Psychological.

(*The caravan goes out.*)

(*It grows dark. A thunderstorm, you would say, is brewing. In the darkness scuffling noises can be heard, breathings. It becomes lighter and now we can see. The* WILD WOODERS *are here!* FERRETS, WEASELS, STOATS *perform weird evolutions as they chant their terrible war song.*)

Toad! Toad! Down with Toad!
Down with the popular, successful Toad!

(*The three* CHIEF CONSPIRATORS *form a mystic circle in the middle and utter this horrid incantation.*)

CHIEF FERRET
Oh, may his bathroom cistern spring a leak!

CHIEF WEASEL
On Sunday morning may his collar squeak!

CHIEF STOAT
May all his laces tie themselves in knots.

CHIEF FERRET
And may his fountain pen make frequent blots!

CHIEF WEASEL

May he forget to wind his watch at night.

CHIEF STOAT

And may his dancing pumps be much too tight!

(*They dance solemnly.*)

THE FERRETS

Every ill which Toad inherits
Will be welcomed by the Ferrets.

ALL

Down with Toad! Down with Toad!

THE WEASELS

Day and night the elder Weasels
Hope that he will have the measles.

ALL

Down with Toad! Down with Toad!

THE STOATS

How the happy little Stoats
Laugh when he is off his oats!

ALL

Down with Toad! Down with Toad!
Toad! Toad! Down with Toad!
Down with the popular, successful Toad!

(*It grows dark again. The* WILD WOODERS *can still be heard chanting their diabolical refrain, but they can no longer be seen. There is a loud clap of thunder; it is daylight again. The* WILD WOODERS *have vanished. Then the "poop-poop" of a motor car is heard, followed by a loud crash. Suddenly in comes a violently excited* ALFRED, *the broken ends of the shafts attached to him, but no caravan.* MOLE *follows.*)

MOLE (*soothingly to* ALFRED)

There, there. There, there. (*But* ALFRED *refuses to "there, there!" He careers round the stage, pursued by the conciliatory* MOLE.) There, there. It's all right, Alfred. (*Very reassuringly*) It's all right.

(RAT *comes in, supporting a dazed* TOAD.)

RAT (*turning and shaking his fist at something*)

You villains! You scoundrels, you highwaymen, you—you—

ALFRED (*still gyrating*)

Road hogs. That's the word. Always come to me if you want the right word. Road hogs.

RAT

You road hogs! I'll have the law of you. Rushing about the country at fifty miles an hour! I'll write to all the papers about you! I'll take you through all the courts! (*Turning anxiously to* TOAD) How are you feeling now, Toady? Mole, come and give us a hand with poor old Toad. I'm afraid he's pretty bad.

MOLE (*catching up* ALFRED *at last*)

There, there. That's all right now, isn't it? (*Going to* RAT)
Poor old Toad. (*He takes his other arm, and together he and*
RAT *conduct the dazed one to a grassy bank and sit him*
gently down.)

ALFRED

I said that no good would come of it, and now you see. A
cataclysm, that's what the whole thing's been.

RAT (*anxiously*)

Speak to us, Toady, old man. How is it?

TOAD (*staring in front of him with a rapt expression*)

Poop-poop! Poop-poop! Poop-poop!

MOLE

What's he saying?

RAT

I think he thinks he's the motor car.

TOAD

Poop-poop!

MOLE (*soothingly*)

It's all right, Mr. Toad. It's all right now.

RAT

We'll make 'em sit up, Toad. We'll have the law of 'em.
We'll get you another little cart. We'll make 'em pay for it.

ALFRED

Another! Oh, thank you, thank you, not at all, don't mention it, only too delighted.

TOAD

Poop-poop! (*Raptly he speaks.*) Glorious, stirring sight! The poetry of motion. The real way to travel. The only way to travel. Here today, in the middle of next week tomorrow. Villages skipped, towns and cities jumped. Always somebody else's horizon. Oh bliss, oh rapture! Oh poop-poop!

RAT

Oh, stop being an ass, Toad.

TOAD (*dreamily*)

And to think that I never knew. All those wasted years that lie behind me, I never knew, never even dreamt. But now that I know, now that I fully realize—ah, now! Oh, what a flowery track lies spread before me henceforth. What savory dust clouds shall spring up behind me as I speed on my restless way, what luscious and entrancing smells. What carts I shall fling carelessly into the ditch in the wake of my magnificent onset. Horrid little carts, common carts, canary-colored carts!

RAT

Now look here, Toad, pull yourself together. We'll go to the police station and see if they know anything about that motor car, and then we'll lodge a complaint against the owners, and we'll go to a wheelwright's and have the cart fetched and mended and put to rights, and we'll—

TOAD

Police station? Complaint? Me complain of that beautiful, that heavenly vision which has been vouchsafed me? Mend the cart? I've done with carts forever. Horrid little carts, common carts, canary-colored carts!

MOLE (*hopelessly*)

What are we to do with him?

TOAD

Oh, Ratty. Oh, my good friend Mr. Mole. You can't think how obliged I am to you for coming with me on this glorious trip. I wouldn't have gone without you, and then I might never have seen that—that swan, that star, that thunderbolt. I might never have heard that entrancing sound, nor smelt that bewitching smell. I owe it all to you, my dear, my very dear friends.

RAT (*sadly*)

I see what it is. I recognize the symptoms. He is in the grip of a new craze.

(*Faintly the* FERRETS *and the* STOATS *and the* WEASELS *are heard singing* "Down with Toad! Down with Toad! Down with the popular, successful Toad!")

TOAD (*raptly*)

Poop-poop!

RAT (*to* MOLE)

Well, come along. Let's get him home.

MOLE

Come on, Alfred.

ALFRED (*sadly*)

One of the most distressing cases which has come under our notice. Very sad. Very sad.

TOAD

Poop-poop!

(*They trudge off. As soon as they are gone, the bank is alive again with the* WILD WOODERS, *who burst into mocking laughter.*)

ACT II

Scene 1

THE WILD WOOD

SCENE. *The middle of the Wild Wood. It is an awesome place in the moonlight with the snow thick upon the ground, cold, silent, threatening. Yet not altogether silent, that is the worst of it. You feel that there are hidden watchers behind the trees, waiting to jump out at you. You hear, or seem to hear, their stealthy movements. There is a sudden rustling, and then silence. A twig cracks. Somebody is breathing.*

Now at last we can recognize somebody. It is TOAD, *in motoring gloves and goggles, coming anxiously through the trees, with many a sudden stop and furtive glance over his shoulder. We can hear, and he hears too, a murmur of unseen voices, which rises in a sort of chant until at last we can distinguish the words.*

CHORUS OF WILD WOODERS
> Toad! Toad! Down with Toad!
> Down with the popular, successful Toad!

TOAD (*alarmed*)
W-what's that?

39

(*Mocking laughter answers him.*)
Pah!

(*Dead silence.*)

I said Pah! (*Nervously*) A-and Bah! (*Loudly*) Bah! (*There is an echoing "Bah."*) What's that? (*Again the echo of the last word comes back to him, and he laughs, but a little uneasily.*) Silly of me. Just an echo. Something to do with the acoustics. I must tell Rat. He'd be interested.

> CHORUS (*softly*)
> Toad! Toad! Down with Toad!
> Down with the gallant and courageous Toad!

> TOAD (*sharply*)

Who said that?

(*Mocking laughter answers him.*)

I can see you.

(*Dead silence.*)

Very funny, aren't you? I suppose you think I'm afraid? (*Loudly*) I said I suppose you think I'm afraid? (*There is an echoing "afraid."*) There you are, it's nothing. Just an echo. Listen. (*Hand to mouth*) Rat!

(*Dead silence.*)

Perhaps it doesn't work sometimes. Something to do with the direction of the wind. I'll try again (*Very loudly*) RAT!

> A SOLEMN VOICE

Mole! (*And then a burst of laughter.*)

> CHORUS (*in quick, businesslike time*)
> Toad! Toad! Down with Toad!
> Down with the terrified and timorous Toad!

TOAD

C-c-come and do it. C-come and do it if you dare. (*The mocking laughter again*) Yes, that's all you can do, laugh. Anyone can laugh. Ha-ha-ha-ha-ha! Very funny, isn't it?

A VOICE

Where are you going, Toad?

TOAD

Never you mind where I'm going. I'm going to see Badger, that's where I'm going. (*More confidently as he thinks of Badger*) My friend, Mr. Badger. I'm calling on my old and valued boon companion, the fierce and terrible Badger. (*Loud laughter*)

A LOW VOICE

Where are you going to, my pretty Toad?

A HIGH VOICE

Just a little way down the road.

A LOW VOICE

Why are you wearing your bonnet and shawl?

A HIGH VOICE

Because I am paying an evening call.

A LOW VOICE

Knock at the door, for here's the house.

A HIGH VOICE

Ah! Good evening, Mr. Mouse.
(*There is another burst of laughter.*)

A VOICE

Badger doesn't live here, Toad.

TOAD (*desperately, greeting an imaginary friend*)
Yes, he does; there he is. Ah, my dear Badger, how are you?
No, not at all. Yes, delighted, quite so, no, yes, not in the
least. Fancy! Ha, ha! Well, yes, just a little walk through
the wood. Oh, do you think so? And you're looking splendid
yourself. Never saw you look fiercer. (*Loudly*) I said
fiercer! (*As he goes off*) This way, my dear Badger!

A VOICE
Good-bye, Toad.

A HIGH VOICE (*answering*)
Good-bye!

A VOICE
Good-bye, Mouse.

A SQUEAKY VOICE (*answering*)
Good-bye!

(*There is a last shout of laughter as* TOAD *disappears.*)

CHORUS (*softly*)
  Toad! Toad! Down with Toad!
  Chilblains and Mumps to the Miserable Toad!
  Toad! Toad! Down with Toad!
  Frostbite and Hiccups to the Miserable Toad!

(*The chant goes on, a murmur of unseen voices whose words we can no longer distinguish. In a little while we can hear nothing, and yet it seems that at any moment we shall hear something. No wonder that* MOLE, *limping through the trees, keeps looking over his shoulder.*)

MOLE (*hopefully*)

Ratty! (*In sudden panic*) What's that? (*The movements stop.*) Pooh! It's nothing. I'm not frightened. . . . I do wish Ratty was here. He's so comforting, is Ratty. Or the brave Mr. Toad. He'd frighten them all away. (*He seems to hear the sound of mocking laughter.*) What's that? (*He looks round anxiously.*) Ratty always said, "Don't go into the Wild Wood." That's what he always said. "Not by yourself," he said. "It isn't safe," he said. "We never do," he said. That's what Ratty said. But I thought I knew better. There he was, dear old Rat, dozing in front of the fire; and I thought if I just slipped out, just to see what the Wild Wood was like—(*He breaks off suddenly and darts round, fearing an attack from behind. There is nothing.*) I should be safer up against a tree. Why didn't I think of that before? (*He settles himself at the foot of a tree.*) Ratty would have thought of it, he's so wise. Oh, Ratty, I wish you were here. It's so much more friendly with two. (*His head droops on his chest.*)

A VOICE (*from far off*)

Moly! Moly!

MOLE (*waking up suddenly*)

What's that?

A VOICE

Moly!

MOLE (*frightened*)

Who is it?

A VOICE

Moly! Moly! Moly! Where are you? It's me. It's old Rat.

(RAT *appears; a lantern in his hand, a couple of pistols in his belt, and a cudgel over his shoulder.*)

MOLE (*almost in tears*)

Oh, Rat! Oh, Rat!

RAT (*patting him on the back*)

There, there, there.

MOLE

Oh, Ratty, I've been so frightened, you can't think.

RAT

I know, I know. You shouldn't have gone and done it, Mole. I did my best to keep you from it. We River Bankers hardly ever come, except in couples.

MOLE

But you've come by yourself. Ah, but then that's because you're so brave.

RAT

It isn't just bravery, it's knowing. There are a hundred things you have to know which we understand about, and you don't as yet. I mean passwords and signs, and sayings which have power and effect, and plants you carry in your pocket, and verses you repeat backwards, and dodges and tricks you practice; all simple enough if you know them, but if you don't, you'll find yourself in trouble. Of course if you're Badger it's different.

MOLE

Surely the brave Mr. Toad wouldn't mind coming here by himself?

RAT (*laughing*)

Old Toad? He wouldn't show his face here alone, not for a whole hatful of guineas, Toad wouldn't.

MOLE

Oh, Rat! It is comforting to hear somebody laugh again.

RAT

Poor old Mole. What a rotten time you've had. Never mind, we'll soon be home now. How would a little mulled ale strike you, after you've got into slippers, of course? I made the fire up specially.

MOLE

You think of everything, Ratty.

RAT

Well, shall we start?

MOLE

Oh, Ratty. I don't know how to tell you, and I'm afraid you'll never want me for a companion again, but I can't, I simply can't go all that way now.

RAT

Tired?

MOLE

Aching all over. Oh, Ratty, do forgive me. I feel as if I must just sit here for ever and ever and ever, I'm not a bit frightened now you're with me. And—and I think I want to go to sleep.

RAT

That's all right. But we can't stop here. (*He looks round about him.*) Suppose we go and dig in that mound there, and see if we can't make some sort of a shelter out of the snow and the wind, and have a good rest. And then start for home a bit later on. How's that?

MOLE (*meekly*)

Just as you like.

RAT

Come on, then.

(*He leads the way to the mound, and* MOLE, *following, trips up suddenly and falls over with a squeal.*)

MOLE

Oh, my leg! Oh, my poor shin! Oo!

RAT

Poor old Mole, you don't see to be having much luck today, do you? What is it? Hurt your shin? Let's have a look at it.

MOLE

I must have tripped over a stump or something. Oh my. Oh my.

RAT

It's a very clean cut. That was never done by a stump. Looks like the sharp edge of something metal. Funny.

MOLE

Well, never mind what done it. It hurts just the same whatever done it.

RAT

Wait a moment. (*He begins scratching in the snow.*)

MOLE

What is it?

RAT

I thought so.

MOLE (*still nursing his leg*)

What is it?

RAT

Come and see.

MOLE (*hobbling up*)

Hullo, a door scraper! How very careless of somebody.

RAT

But don't you see what it means?

MOLE (*sitting down again and rubbing his shin*)

Of course I see what it means. It means that some very forgetful person has left his door scraper lying about in the middle of the Wild Wood just where it's sure to trip everybody up. Somebody ought to write to him about it.

RAT

Oh, Mole, how stupid you are. (*He begins scratching busily again.*) There! What's that?

MOLE (*examining it closely*)

It looks like a door mat.

RAT

It *is* a door mat. And what does that tell you?

MOLE

Nothing, Rat, nothing. Who ever heard of a door mat telling anyone anything? They simply don't do it. They are not that sort at all. They—what have you found now?

(RAT, *still at it, has now disclosed a solid-looking little door, dark green, with a brass plate on it.*)

RAT (*proudly*)

There! (*He fetches the lantern and holds it up to the plate.*)
What do you read there?

MOLE (*awestruck*)

"Mr. Badger. Seventh Wednesdays."—Rat!

RAT (*proudly*)

What do you think of that?

MOLE

Rat, you're a wonder, that's what you are! I see it all now.
You argued it out step by step from the moment when I fell
and cut my shin, and you looked at the cut, and your
majestic mind said to itself, "Door scraper." Did it stop
there? No. Your powerful brain went on working. It said
to itself—

RAT (*impatiently*)

Yes, yes, well now let's—

MOLE (*going on sleepily and happily*)

Your powerful brain said to itself, "Where there's a scraper,
there must be a mat."

RAT

Quite so. And now—

MOLE

"I have noticed before," said the wise Mr. Rat,
"That where there's a scraper there must be a mat."
And did you stop there? No. Your intellect still went on

working. It said grandly to itself, "Where there's a door
mat there must be a door."

RAT

Exactly. And now that we've found it—

MOLE

Said the wise Mr. Rat, "I have noticed before,
That where there's a door mat there must be a door."
You know, Rat, you're simply wasted here amongst us
fellows. If I only had your head—

RAT

But as you haven't, I suppose you are going to sit on the
snow and talk all night. Now wake up a bit and hang on to
this bellpull, while I hammer.

MOLE (*sleepily*)

Oh, all right.
    Said the wise Mr. Rat, "I have often heard tell
    That where there's a bellpull there must be a bell."

(*He hangs on to the bellpull, while* RAT *hammers on
the door with his cudgel. Down in* MR. BADGER'S *house
a deep-toned bell responds.*)

Scene 2

BADGER'S HOUSE

Scene. badger's *underground home. The room which we see is one of those delightful mixtures of hall, kitchen, drawing room, dining room, larder and pantry. In the middle of the room, says Mr. Kenneth Grahame, but we shall probably put it to one side, stands a long table of plain boards on trestles, with benches drawn up to it. There is a big open fireplace with high-backed settles on each side; an armchair in which the owner can read* The Times, *and is now so doing. The floor is brick. From the rafters hang hams, nets of onions and bundles of herbs. In short, a place where heroes can feast after victory, harvesters keep their Harvest Home with mirth and song, and two or three friends sit about as they please in comfort and content. There are three doors, labelled* front door, back door, *and* study. *At a knocking on the back door a convulsion passes over* The Times; *at a second knocking it stands on end; and at a third* mr. badger *comes out from behind the leading article. Grumbling to himself, for his after-supper nap has been disturbed, he goes to the door.*

BADGER (*opening the door*)

Well, well, well, what is it, what is it? (*A collection of field mice, half a dozen of them in red mufflers, stand nervously shuffling at the entrance.*)

FIRST FIELD MOUSE (*huskily*)

Oh, please, Mr. Badger, did you want any carols?

BADGER

Any what? Speak up!

FIRST FIELD MOUSE (*swallowing*)

Carols.

BADGER

Let's have a look at them.

SECOND FIELD MOUSE (*striking up*)

"Good King Wenceslas looked out—"

BADGER

Oh, I thought you said carrots. Run along, all of you. Time you were in bed.

SECOND FIELD MOUSE

"Good King Wenceslas looked out—"

BADGER

And if you come round disturbing me again, you'll have to look out. Now then, off you go.

FIRST FIELD MOUSE

Oh, please, Mr. Badger, we always used to sing carols to Mr. Mole, and he used to ask us in, and give us hot drinks, and supper too sometimes.

SECOND FIELD MOUSE (*proudly*)

We had steak-and-kidney pudding once.

FIRST FIELD MOUSE

That's right, sir.

SECOND FIELD MOUSE

Real steak-and-kidney pudding with kidney in it.

FIRST FIELD MOUSE

That was Mr. Mole, sir. Down at Mole End. Always asked us in, Mr. Mole did.

BADGER

Ah! Mole did, did he? And Mole is a very sensible young animal. I have great hopes of Mole. Well, run away now, but come back in twenty minutes when I'm not so busy, and perhaps I'll let you sing me the—what did you call it?

FIELD MICE (*eagerly*)

Carol.

BADGER

Carol. I thought you said carrot. Well, then, you can sing me the one that Mr. Mole liked, and if I like it too, I won't say that perhaps there won't be a bit of hot something for one or two of you, the ones that don't snuffle, that is, and—

FIELD MICE

Oh, thank you, Mr. Badger.

BADGER

Now then, run along, there's good children. (*They run along.*) So Mole likes carols, does he? (*He goes back to his chair, and covers his face up again.*) Likes carols, does he? (*He breathes heavily.*) Carols. . . . Thought he said carrots. (*He snores. . . . But he is not to sleep long. This time it is the front-door bell which rings; again and again. There is a hammering, too, at the door. Very much annoyed,* BADGER *gets to his feet.*)

BADGER

All right, all right, all right! What is it, who is it? (*He opens the front door.*) Speak up!

RAT

Hallo, Badger. It's me, Rat, and my friend Mole, and we've lost our way in the snow. Mole's that tired you never did.

BADGER

Well, well, well. Rat and his friend Mole. (*He brings them in.*) Come along in, both of you, at once. Why, you must be perished! Well, I never! Lost in the snow. And your friend that tired. Well, well. And in the Wild Wood at this time of night! (*He pats their heads paternally.*) I'm afraid you've been up to some of your pranks again, Ratty. But come along in. There's a good fire here, and supper and everything.

MOLE (*as he sees the supper-table*)

Oo, I say! (*He nudges* RAT *in an anticipatory sort of way.*)

BADGER

Now what will you do first? Toast your toes a bit? (*He removes* The Times.) I was just glancing at the paper. Or supper now and toast your toes afterwards? It's all ready. I was expecting one or two friends might drop in.

MOLE (*shyly*)

I think I should like supper at once, please, Mr. Badger.

BADGER

That's right, Mole. Sensible animal. And what about you, Rat?

RAT (*who is standing with his back to the fire, as an old friend should*)

Just as you like. Fine old place this, isn't it, Mole?

MOLE (*already among the plates*)

Grand. (*He sits down to it.* RAT *fetches himself a sandwich and gets his back to the fire again.* BADGER, *in an armchair, beams upon them kindly.*)

BADGER (*to* RAT)

Won't your friend try some of those pickles?

RAT

Try a pickle, Mole.

MOLE (*his mouth full*)

Thanks. (*He helps himself.*)

BADGER (*solemnly, after a silence broken only by the noise of eating*)

I've been wanting to see you fellows because I have heard very grave reports of our mutual friend, Toad.

RAT (*sadly*)
Oh, Toad. (*He shakes his head.*)

MOLE (*as sympathetically as he can with a mouth full of pickles*)
Tut-tut-tut.

BADGER
Is his case as hopeless as one has heard?

RAT
Going from bad to worse. That's all you can say about him, isn't it, Mole?

MOLE (*nodding busily*)
Mmm. (*Swallowing hastily.*) That's all.

RAT
Another smash up only last week, and a bad one. You see, since he's got this motor craze, he will insist on driving himself, and he's hopelessly incapable. If he'd only employ a decent, steady, well-trained animal, pay him good wages and leave everything to him, he'd get on all right. But no, he's convinced he's the greatest driver ever, and nobody can teach him anything. And so it goes on.

MOLE
And so it goes on.

BADGER (*gloomily*)

And so it goes on. (*After a pause*) How many has he had?

RAT

Cars or smashes? Oh well, it's the same thing with Toad. The last was the seventh.

MOLE

He's been in hospital three times, and as for the fines he's had to pay—

RAT

Toad's rich, we all know, but he's not a millionaire. Killed or ruined, it will be one or the other with Toad.

BADGER

Alas! Alas! I knew his father. I knew his grandfather. Many's the time— (*A sob chokes him.*) Alas, poor witless animal!

MOLE (*still busy*)

You really ought to try a slice of this beef, Rat.

RAT

No thanks, really.

MOLE

Don't know when I've tasted better.

RAT (*to* BADGER)

Oughtn't we to do something? We're his friends.

BADGER

Yes, you're right. The hour has come.

MOLE (*anxiously*)

What hour?

BADGER

Whose hour, you should say. Toad's hour. The hour of Toad.

RAT (*quietly*)

Well done, Badger. I knew you'd feel that way too.

MOLE (*firmly*)

We'll teach him to be a sensible Toad.

BADGER

At any moment another new and exceptionally powerful motor car will arrive at Toad Hall for approval or return. We must be up and doing ere it is too late.

RAT

That's right, Badger. We'll rescue the poor unhappy animal. We'll convert him. He'll be the most converted Toad that ever was before we've finished with him.

BADGER

The first step is to get him here and reason with him. You know how it is. In the present weather I don't go about much. Naturally.

RAT

Of course not.

MOLE

Of course not.

BADGER

But once Toad is here—

RAT

How to get him, that's the problem.

BADGER (*gravely*)

Let us apply our minds to it.

> (*They apply their minds. Absent-mindedly, while thinking,* MOLE *helps himself to beef. Suddenly the bell rings loudly.*)

BADGER

Whoever's that? (*He shuffles off to the door and as he opens it* TOAD *falls into his arms, panting with fear.*)

RAT (*in surprise*)

Why, it's Toad!

MOLE

Hallo, Toad, you ought to try some of this beef.

RAT

Why, what's the matter? (TOAD, *supported by* BADGER, *falls limply into a chair and sits there panting.*) Another accident? (TOAD *shakes his head.*) That's something.

TOAD (*still panting a little*)

Ah, Ratty, my dear old Ratty, and my good friend Mole, how badly I seemed to need your help just now. What would I not have given to have had you by my side. As it was, I had to do the best I could without you. Fortunately it was enough. But as you see, it has exhausted me somewhat.

RAT

What's happened? Wild Wooders?

TOAD (*warming to it*)

An unfortunate breakdown in my car, a loose nut, some trifling mishap, left me stranded at the edge of the wood, far from home. I bethought me of my good friend Mr. Badger; he would lend me a sleeping suit and put me up for the night. As I came whistling through the wood, recking nought of danger, I was suddenly seized upon by a gang of rascally ferrets. I set about them lightheartedly, at the most there were no more than a dozen of them, when suddenly, to my horror, they were reinforced by a posse of scoundrelly weasels. It was then, Ratty, and my dear friend Mole, that I wished I had your assistance. Twelve of the rascals, yes (*He is now standing up, legs straddled, and enjoying himself immensely.*) but twenty-four of them is a different matter. If only you and Mole could have taken a couple of them off my hands, there might have been a different story to tell. As it was, a rear guard action was forced upon me. Step by step . . . (*He realizes a faint hostile something in the air, particularly from the direction of* BADGER. *He goes on less confidently.*) Step by step . . . (*He looks from one to the other, hoping for a little encouragement, but the atmosphere is now really terrible; nobody could tell even the simplest story in it. He makes a last desperate effort.*) Step by step . . .

BADGER (*solemnly*)
Won't you sit down again, Toad?

TOAD (*meekly*)
Thank you.

RAT
Would you care to be nearer the fire?

TOAD (*faintly*)
No, thank you.

MOLE
Let me put your gloves down for you.

TOAD
It's all right, thank you.

BADGER (*to* RAT)
The moment has come, I think, don't you?

RAT
I think so.

BADGER (*to* MOLE)

You agree?

MOLE

Yes. (*He sighs.*)

TOAD (*uneasily*)

I say, you fellows, what's all this? (*He catches* BADGER'S *eye and is silent again.*)

BADGER (*solemnly*)

Toad. I knew your father, worthy animal that he was; I knew your grandfather. It was also my privilege to be slightly acquainted with your uncle, the Archdeacon; of that I shall speak further directly. The question I wish to ask you now is this. At the beginning of the breathless story of adventure to which we have just been listening, you mentioned (*He pauses dramatically.*) a motor car. You implied further that this motor car had suddenly lost its efficiency. Am I right in supposing that just at this moment your narrative hovered for an instant on the confines of truth?

TOAD (*sulkily*)

What do you mean?

RAT

Really, Toad, he couldn't have put it more plainly.

BADGER

I asked you, Toad, if it is indeed a fact that your eighth

motor car is now in as fragmentary a condition as the previous seven?

TOAD (*sulkily*)
I had a little accident.

BADGER
Thank you. (*To* RAT) Then I think that in that case we may begin the treatment?

RAT
Yes, I think so.

BADGER (*to* MOLE)
You agree?

MOLE
Yes.

TOAD
I say, you fellows—

BADGER
Toad! (TOAD *looks at him.*) Rise from your chair a moment. (TOAD *rises.*) Rat, Mole, may I trouble you a moment? (*He indicates that he wants* TOAD's *chair in a position where he can be harangued better. They rise to move it.*) Thank you. . . . There, I think. . . . Perhaps just a trifle more to the left. . . . Thank you. Toad! (*He points to the chair and* TOAD *meekly creeps into it.*)

RAT (*kindly*)

This is all for your good, Toady old man.

BADGER

Now then, first of all take those ridiculous goggles off.

TOAD (*plucking up courage*)

Shan't! What is the meaning of this gross outrage? I demand an instant explanation.

BADGER

Take them off then, you two.

RAT (*as* TOAD *looks like showing fight*)

It's all for your own good, Toady old man. We've been talking it over for hours. Might as well take it quietly.

MOLE

We don't like doing it, Toad, really we don't. It's only because we are so fond of you. (*They remove the goggles.*)

BADGER

That is better. It was thus that your father knew you. It was thus that your grandfather, had he survived a year or two longer, would have known you. Now then, Toad. You've disregarded all the warnings we've given you, you've gone on squandering the money your father left you, and you're getting us animals a bad name in the district by your furious driving and your smashes and your rows with the police. We have decided, my friend Ratty here and Mole and I, that it is time we saved you from yourself. I am go-

ing to make one more effort to bring you to reason. You
will come with me into my study, and there you will hear
some facts about yourself. I say the study, because on second thoughts I have decided, for the sake of your revered
grandfather, to spare you the pain of a public reproof.
Come!

TOAD (*meekly*)

Yes, Badger. Thank you, Badger. (*They go out together.*)

RAT

That's no good! Talking to Toad will never cure him. He'll
say anything.

MOLE

Yes. (*He sighs.*)

RAT

We must do something.

MOLE

Yes. (*He sighs again.*)

RAT (*looking at him suddenly*)

What's the matter, old fellow? You seem melancholy. Too
much beef?

MOLE (*bravely*)

Oh, no, it isn't that. It was just—no, never mind, I shall be
all right directly. (*He wipes away a tear.*)

RAT

Why, whatever is it?

MOLE

Nothing, Ratty, nothing. I was just admiring Badger's great big house and comparing it with my own little home, which —which I haven't seen lately. Just comparing it, you know, and thinking about it; and thinking about it, and comparing it. Not meaning to, you know. Just happening to—think about it.

RAT (*remorsefully*)

Oh, Mole.

MOLE (*in a sudden burst*)

I know it's a shabby, dingy little place; not like your cozy quarters, or Toad's beautiful Hall, or Badger's great house. But it was my own little home and I was fond of it; and I went away and forgot all about it. And since we've been down here it's all been coming back to me. Perhaps it's the pickles. I always had Military Pickles too. I shall be better soon. I don't know what you'll think of me.

RAT (*patting him on the back*)

Poor old Mole. Been rather an exciting day, hasn't it? And then the same sort of pickles. Tell me about Mole End. We might go and pay it a visit tomorrow if you've nothing better to do.

MOLE

It wouldn't be fine enough for you. You're used to great

big places and fine houses. I noticed directly we came in how you stood with your back to the fire so grandly and easily, just as if it were nothing to you.

RAT

Well, you tucked into the beef, old chap.

MOLE

Did I?

RAT

Rather. Made yourself quite at home. I said to myself at once, "Mole is used to going out," I said. "Weekend parties at big country houses," I said, "that's nothing to Mole," I said.

MOLE (*eagerly*)

Did you really, Ratty?

RAT

Oh, rather. Spotted it at once.

MOLE

Of course there were features about Mole End which made it rather, rather . . .

RAT

Rather a feature?

MOLE

Yes. The statuary. I'd picked up a bit of statuary here and

there. You'd hardly think how it livened the place up. Garibaldi, the Infant Samuel and Queen Victoria, dotted about in odd corners. It had a very pleasing effect, my friends used to tell me.

RAT (*heartily*)

I should like to have seen that, Mole, I should indeed. That must have been very striking.

MOLE

It was just about now that they used to come carol singing.

RAT

Garibaldi and the others?

MOLE

The field mice.

RAT

Oh yes, of course.

MOLE

Quite an institution they were. They never passed me over. Always came to Mole End last, and I gave them hot drinks and supper sometimes, when I could afford it.

RAT

Yes, I remember now hearing about it, and what a fine place Mole End was.

MOLE (*wistfully*)

Did you? It wasn't very big.

RAT

Between ourselves, I don't much care about these big places. Cozy and tasteful, that's what I always heard about Mole End.

MOLE (*squeezing* RAT's *paw*)
You're a good friend, Ratty. I like being with you.

RAT
Good old Mole.

(*They are happily silent together. Suddenly, faint and far-off and sweet, a carol can be heard, "the carol that Mr. Mole liked."*)

MOLE
There they are!

(*They listen raptly. When it is over they give a little sigh, for it is time now to get back to business. The door opens and* BADGER *comes in, leading by the paw a very dejected* TOAD.)

BADGER (*kindly*)
Sit down there, Toad. (TOAD *sits down.*) My friends, I am pleased to inform you that Toad has at last seen the error of his ways. He is truly sorry for his misguided conduct in the past, and he has undertaken to give up motor cars entirely and forever in the future. I have his solemn promise to that effect.

MOLE (*eagerly*)
Oh Toad, I am glad!

RAT (*doubtfully*)
H'm!

BADGER
There is only one thing which remains to be done. Toad, I want you solemnly to repeat before your friends here what you fully admitted to me in the study just now. First, you are sorry for what you have done and see the folly of it all?

(*There is an anxious silence.*)

TOAD (*suddenly*)
No! I'm not sorry. And it wasn't folly at all. It was simply glorious!

BADGER (*horrified*)
What?

MOLE
Toady!

RAT
I thought so.

BADGER
You back-sliding animal, didn't you tell me just now in there—

TOAD

Oh yes, yes, in there. I'd have said anything in there. You're so eloquent, dear Badger, and so moving, and so convincing, and put all your points so frightfully well; you can do what you like with me in there. But, thinking it over out here, I see that I am not a bit sorry really, so it's no earthly good saying I am, now is it?

BADGER

Then you don't promise never to touch a motor car again?

TOAD

Of course I don't. On the contrary, I faithfully promise that the very first motor car I see, poop-poop, off I go in it!

RAT (*to* MOLE)

I told you so.

BADGER

Very well then. Since you won't yield to persuasion, we'll try what force can do. I feared it would come to this all along. You'll stay with me, Toad, until a cure has been effected. My friends, Rat and Mole, will also stay with me and help me to look after you. It's going to be a tedious business but we will see it out. (*He takes down a large key from the wall and picking up the lantern, leads the way to the guest chamber.*) Bring him along. (*They bring him along. The procession goes slowly, and on* TOAD's *part reluctantly, out.*)

Scene 3

THE SAME. SOME WEEKS LATER

SCENE. *Badger's home on a spring morning some weeks later.* MR. BADGER *is in an armchair, with his feet on another, reading a newspaper, and paying no attention whatever to* TOAD, *who is in the paroxysms of another attack.* TOAD (*poor fellow*) *has arranged three chairs in a hopeful representation of a motor car. He sits on the front one grasping an imaginary wheel, changing imaginary gears and making appropriate noises. A sudden* (*imaginary*) *block in the traffic, pulls him up sharply, though his "Hi, look ahead there!" averts an accident. He gets off and winds up his engine, then lifts the bonnet and peers in. In a little while he is off again; but now a real accident upsets him. The chairs are strewn about and* TOAD *lies panting in the wreckage.* BADGER *lifts an eye, glances at him and goes on with his paper.* MOLE *comes in. He looks at* TOAD.

MOLE
Tut-tut. Again?

BADGER (*still reading his paper*)
The third crash this morning. There seems to be a good deal of traffic on the road today.

MOLE

Poor old Toad.

BADGER

I always warned you, my dear Mole, that in these cases the poison takes a long time to work itself out of the system. But we're improving; we're improving daily. Let me see. It's Rat's turn to be on guard this morning, isn't it?

MOLE

Yes. (*He helps* TOAD *up.*) Lean on me, old fellow. That's right. Lie down a bit. (*He assists him towards a camp bed in the corner of the room.*) You'll be better directly. I daresay Rat will read to you if you ask him.

TOAD (*weakly*)

Thank you, my dear friend, thank you. Don't let me be a burden to you.

MOLE

That's all right, Toady. We'll soon get you well.

BADGER

What do you say to a bit of a ramble along the hedgerows, Mole? And there's a new burrow I want to show you. I must say I like being out in this sort of weather.

MOLE (*eagerly*)

Just what I was going to suggest. I wish old Ratty could come too. I suppose . . . (*He looks across at* TOAD.)

BADGER

No, no, it wouldn't be safe. (*In a whisper*) Toad's quiet now, and when he is quiet, then he's at his artfullest. I know him.

MOLE

Yes, I suppose so. But it's such an exciting sort of day. Rat would love it so.

(*Enter* RAT.)

RAT

Hallo, you fellows, not off yet?

BADGER

Just going. (*He gets up.*) Toad's quiet now. But keep an eye on him. I don't trust him.

RAT

That's all right.

MOLE (*quietly to* RAT)

I believe he's worse than Badger thinks. Look after him well, poor old Toad.

RAT

That's all right.

BADGER (*at the door*)

Coming, Mole?

MOLE

Coming. Poor old Ratty, it is a shame being kept in like this. Still we all have our turns.

RAT

Of course we do. Good luck to you.

MOLE

Good-bye!

BADGER

Are you coming, Mole?

MOLE

Coming. Good-bye! Good-bye, Toad!

TOAD (*faintly*)

Good-bye, dear old Mole.

MOLE (*ecstatically*)

What a morning! I don't think I ever remember—

BADGER (*severely*)

When I was young we always had mornings like this.

(*They go out.* RAT, *after getting into an easier coat, turns his attention to* TOAD.)

RAT

Well, how are you today, old chap?

TOAD (*faintly*)

Thank you so much, dear Ratty. It is good of you to inquire. But first tell me how you are yourself?

RAT

Oh, I'm all right.

TOAD

I'm glad. I'm glad. And the excellent Mole?

RAT

Oh, he's all right.

TOAD

Splendid, splendid. And the venerable Badger? He, I trust, is in robust health also?

RAT

Rather. He and Mole have gone out for a ramble together. They won't be back till lunch.

TOAD

Ah. (*Very faintly*) Dear fellows all.

RAT

Now, old boy, we're going to have a jolly morning together, so jump up and I'll do my best to amuse you.

TOAD

Dear, kind Rat, how little you realize my condition, and

how very far I am from jumping up now, if ever. But do not trouble about me. I hate being a burden to my friends, and I do not expect to be one much longer.

RAT

Well, I hope not too. You've been a fine bother to us all this time, you have really, Toad. Weeks and weeks. And now, in weather like this, and the boating season just beginning. It's too bad of you!

TOAD

I'm a nuisance to my friends, I know, I know.

RAT (*wistfully*)

I was thinking about my river yesterday evening, and I— I wrote a little poem. (*Shyly*) Do you think you would like to hear it?

TOAD

As you will, my dear Ratty. It may comfort my last hours.

RAT (*eagerly*)

It's about the ducks. I used to have such fun with them. You know when they stand on their heads suddenly, well, then I dive down and tickle their necks, and they come up all spluttering and angry, and shaking their feathers at me. Of course they aren't angry really, because it's all fun. And then I used to sit on the bank in the sun and pretend I was coming in after 'em again, and— (*He breaks off suddenly and announces*) "Ducks' Ditty."

All along the backwater,
Through the rushes tall,
Ducks are a-dabbling,
Up tails all!

Ducks' tails, drakes' tails,
Yellow feet aquiver,
Yellow bills all out of sight
Busy in the river!

Every one for what he likes!
We like to be
Heads down, tails up.
Dabbling free!

High in the blue above
Swifts whirl and call,
We are down a-dabbling,
Up tails all!

(He looks in front of him, seeing it all.)

TOAD *(with a deep sigh)*
Thank you. I am glad to have heard it. Ratty?

RAT *(waking from his reverie)*
Yes?

TOAD
I wonder if I could bother you. But no, you have been too
kind already.

RAT

Why, what is it? You know we'd do anything for you, all
of us.

TOAD

Then could I beg you, for the last time probably, to step
round to the village as quickly as possible, even now it may
be too late, and fetch the doctor?

RAT (*surprised*)

But—

TOAD

No, you're right. It's only a trouble, and perhaps we may
as well let things take their course.

RAT

But what do you want a doctor for?

TOAD

Surely you have noticed . . . but no, why should you?
Noticing things is only a trouble. Tomorrow, indeed, you
may be saying to yourself, "Oh, if only I had noticed
sooner! If only I had done something. Too late, too late!"
Forget that I asked. Naturally you want to go on with your
poetry. Have you ever done anything in the way of epi-
taphs?

RAT (*alarmed*)

Look here, old man, of course I'll fetch a doctor to you if

you really want one. But it hasn't come to that yet. You're imagining. Now let's talk about something more cheerful.

TOAD (*with an angelic expression*)
I fear, dear friend, that talk can do little in a case like this, or doctors either, for that matter. Still one must grasp at the slightest straw. And by the way, while you are in the village, I hate to bother you, but I fancy that you pass the door—would you mind asking my lawyer to step up? There are moments, perhaps I should say there is a moment, when one must face disagreeable tasks, at whatever cost to exhausted nature. Thank you, my dear fellow, thank you. You will not be forgotten. (*He closes his eyes.*)

RAT
A lawyer! He must be bad. (*Aloud*) All right, Toad, I'll go.

(*He makes his preparations to go out, glancing from time to time at the unconscious* TOAD *as he does so. Then a brilliant idea occurs to him.*)

RAT (*loudly*)
I'm going now, Toad.

TOAD (*faintly, his eyes closed*)
Thank you, thank you.

RAT
I'll bring the doctor and the lawyer, and we'll be back as quickly as we can.

TOAD

You're a good fellow, Ratty.

RAT

Good-bye, old boy. Keep your spirits up.

TOAD

Good-bye.

(*Humming a tune and making a good deal of noise,* RAT *goes out. Then very quietly he steals back again and peers round the door.* TOAD *is apparently still on the verge of dissolution.* RAT *nods to himself in satisfaction with his strategy;* TOAD'S *illness is obviously genuine. We hear him as he starts through the Wild Wood, singing "Ducks' Ditty" to himself. As the song dies in the distance,* TOAD *opens an eye. Then the other eye. He raises his head and listens. He sits up in bed, still listening. Then with a laugh he jumps up and takes the floor.*)

TOAD (*boastfully*)

Ha, ha, ha! Smart piece of work that! (*He chatters to himself as he collects his coat, gloves, goggles, money and other accessories of outdoor life.*) Brain against brute force; and brain came out on the top, as it's bound to do. Poor old Ratty. My! Won't he catch it when Badger gets back! A worthy fellow, Ratty, with many good qualities, but very little intelligence and absolutely no education. I must take him in hand some day and see if I can make something of him. (*He is ready now; as he goes to the door he begins to sing. Really a most conceited song.*)

The world has held great heroes,
  As history books have showed;
But never a name to go down to fame
  Compared with that of Toad!

(*He is singing the last line as he opens the door. Then
with a triumphant* "Poop-poop! Poop-poop!" *he disappears.*)

ACT III

Scene 1

THE COURTHOUSE

Scene. *The Courthouse. A bare, clean, whitewashed room, furnished with a Bench, a Jury box, and a little extra space for the witnesses and spectators. It is crowded today, for the notorious* TOAD *is to be tried, and there is every prospect that he will be sentenced to a severe term of penal servitude. In one corner, sitting glomily together, are* BADGER, RAT, *and* MOLE. BADGER *has his handkerchief out. On the Bench the* JUDGE, *an owl-like gentleman, is sitting, sipping a cup of tea. A figure, its head bowed in its hands, sits beside him. An* USHER, *tall and thin, wanders round the room with a list in his hand, ticking off those present. In the Jury box a* TURKEY, *a* DUCK, *four* SQUIRRELS, *five* RABBITS *and the* CHIEF WEASEL *are crowded together.*

USHER

One Judge. (*He looks at the Bench and marks off the* JUDGE *on his list.*) Twelve Jury. (*He counts them and marks them off.*) One policeman witness. (*To* POLICEMAN) That's you. Now, don't you go a-moving or you'll muddle me. One

policeman, and one prisoner. (*He looks at the Dock.*) Hallo!
That's funny. Where is the prisoner?

POLICEMAN (*staggered*)

Well, I know I brought him in. (*Loudly*) Toad! Where
are you?

TOAD (*looking up from the Bench, sadly*)

Here I am.

USHER

What yer doing there? Come down out of it.

TOAD (*meekly*)

I thought this was where the prisoners went. (*He glances at
the* JUDGE, *and comes down with a smirk.*)

EVERYBODY

Did you hear what he said. . . . What was it? . . . Well,
of all the cheek. . . . Just like Toad. . . . What was it?
I didn't hear. . . .

(*And now, all being present, the* USHER *walks up to the*
JUDGE *and whispers in his ear. The* JUDGE *finishes his
tea and nods.*)

USHER

Silence!

EVERYBODY (*to everybody else*)

Silence! Silence!

JUDGE (*annoyed*)
Stop saying "Silence!"

EVERYBODY (*to everybody else*)
Stop saying "Silence!"

JUDGE
It's worse than ever! (*To* USHER) Try them with "Hush!"

USHER (*in a loud whisper*)
Hush!
(*Everybody hushes.*)

JUDGE
Please understand, once and for all, that unless I have complete hush, it will be impossible for the prisoner to be tried.

TOAD
I don't want to be tried.

JUDGE (*sternly*)
Impossible for him to be tried, but not impossible for him to be severely sentenced.

BADGER (*in tears*)
Alack! Alack! Oh hapless Toad!

TOAD
Well, it was fun anyway.

JUDGE (*clearing his throat*)
H'm. Friends and fellow citizens. We see before us, cower-

ing in the Dock, one of the most notorious and hardened malefactors of our time, the indigenous Toad.

TOAD

I'm not indigenous.

JUDGE (*grimly*)

Well, if you're not, you very soon will be. We see before us, I say, this monster of iniquity, and it is our duty to try him fairly and without prejudice; and to sentence him to the very sharpest term of imprisonment that we can think of, so as to learn him not to do it again. We shall then adjourn for lunch. (*Cries of "Hear, hear."*) It may be that after lunch we shall see things in a more rosy light and be tempted to dilute justice with mercy, to the extent of remitting some thirty or forty years of the sentence. If so, we shall fight against the temptation. If, on the other hand, we see things in a more somber light, and realize suddenly that we have been too lenient with the cowering criminal before us, we shall not hesitate to remedy our error. (*Kindly*) Has the prisoner anything to say before we pass on?

TOAD (*meekly*)

No.

JUDGE

Very well. Then I proceed to the charge. The counts against the prisoner are as follows. (*To* USHER) By the way, is the Jury all present? I particularly want the Jury to hear this. Just call 'em out and see.

USHER
Certainly, my lord. Mr. Turkey.

TURKEY
Here!

USHER
Mr. Duck.

DUCK
Here!

USHER
Four squirrels.

SQUIRRELS
Here!

USHER
Six rabbits.

RABBITS
Here!

(RAT *rises and holds up his hand.*)

RAT (*firmly*)
I object. (*Sensation.*)

JUDGE (*putting on his glasses*)
What's the matter? Who is it? What did he—Ah, Ratty, my little friend, is it you? Delighted to see you. If you will

just wait until I have got this ruffian off my hands, we can have a little talk. What about lunching with me? (*To* USHER) Go on, please.

USHER
Six rabbits.

RABBITS
Here!

RAT
I object, my lord.

JUDGE (*surprised*)
Object?

RAT
One of the rabbits is a weasel.

CHIEF WEASEL (*indignantly*)
I'm not! I'm a rabbit.

RAT
He's a weasel.

JUDGE
Dear, dear. A difference of opinion. (*To* USHER) What are we to do? What does one do?

USHER
He says he's a rabbit, my lord, and he ought to know.

JUDGE (*to* RAT)

There's something in that. You can't make a mistake about a thing of that sort.

RAT (*doggedly*)

He's a weasel.

CHIEF WEASEL

I'm not!

RAT

That proves it. (*To* WEASEL) Why should you say you aren't, if you aren't?

JUDGE

But of course he says he aren't if he aren't. I mean if he aren't, then he aren't, so naturally he says he aren't. (*He fans himself with his handkerchief.*)

RAT

But he wouldn't say he wasn't, if he wasn't. The other rabbits didn't say they wasn't. Why didn't they say they wasn't? Because they aren't.

JUDGE (*to* USHER)

Just make a note that I shall want a glass of iced water if this goes on.

RAT (*eagerly*)

Of course if you aren't, you don't say you aren't, but if you weren't, you would say you were.

JUDGE (*completely muddled*)

But you wouldn't say you aren't, if you weren't, and on the other hand— (*Despairingly*) I think we'd better begin this trial all over again.

USHER

Yes, my lord. Much the best way.

JUDGE (*to* RAT)

You can tell me your objections afterwards, when we have this desperate ruffian safely lodged in a dungeon.

RAT

He's a weasel. I know he's a weasel. You can see he's a weasel. It isn't fair!

JUDGE (*soothingly*)

There, there, there. We'll talk about it calmly at lunch. There's a nice saddle of mutton, and red currant jelly.

MOLE (*boldly*)

It's a shame, that's what it is, when everybody knows what the weasels are.

CHIEF WEASEL (*to the* RABBITS)

I'm a rabbit, aren't I a rabbit? (*Under his breath*) Say I am, quick!

RABBITS (*terrified*)

Y-yes.

CHIEF WEASEL

There you are. Naturally there are lots of different kinds of rabbit, and I'm one of the different kinds.

RAT

No, you're not.

CHIEF WEASEL

Yes, I am.

JUDGE

Please, please! For my sake. (*To* USHER) Now then, all over again.

USHER (*stolidly*)

Mr. Turkey.

TURKEY

Here!

USHER

Mr. Duck.

DUCK

Here!

USHER

Four squirrels.

SQUIRRELS

Here!

USHER
Five ordinary rabbits.

RABBITS
Here!

USHER
One different kind of rabbit.

CHIEF WEASEL
Here!

USHER
That's the lot, my lord.

ALFRED (*suddenly appearing*)
What about me?

JUDGE (*putting on his glasses*)
What is this?

ALFRED (*in the* USHER'S *voice*)
Alfred. (*Squeakily*) Here!

JUDGE (*to the* POLICEMAN)
Lead it out.

ALFRED (*as he is led out*)
All right, all right. I only just looked in. No *esprit de corps.*
That's what's the matter with them all. No *esprit de corps.*

JUDGE

Now then. (*Looking at his watch*) We haven't too much
time. The counts against the prisoner are as follows: First,
that he did maliciously steal a valuable motor car without
so much as a "with your leave" or a "by your leave." Second, that being in the said motor car, he did drive recklessly
and to the common danger. Third, that on being appre-
hended he was guilty of gross impertinence to the rural
police. (*Cheerfully*) Now then, Toad, what have you got
to say about all that?

TOAD

I wasn't driving recklessly. I was just going along quietly
at about seventy miles an hour, when I saw a policeman in
front of me. Naturally I quickened up to see if he wanted
anything. Same as anyone else would have done who's fond
of policemen.

POLICEMAN

Recklessly and to the common danger.

TOAD

Rubbish!

POLICEMAN

And what did you call me, eh?

TOAD

How can I remember? Officer, constable, sergeant—

POLICEMAN

No, you didn't.

JUDGE

Now we're getting at it. What did he call you?

POLICEMAN (*annoyed*)

He called me fat-face.

(*Sensation.*)

JUDGE (*aghast*)

Fat-face!

EVERYBODY (*to everybody else*)

He called him fat-face!

JUDGE

This is terrible. This adds years to my life. (*To* POLICEMAN) You mean to tell me that this ruffian, this incorrigible rogue whom I am about to sentence to a severe term of penal servitude, had the audacity to call a representative of the Law "fat-face"?

RAT

Oh, Toady!

BADGER

Alack! Alack! Oh hapless animal!

JUDGE

Fat-face. Did I hear it aright? Fat-face?

POLICEMAN (*sulkily*)

We don't want to make a song about it. I told you what he called me, and that's what he called me.

USHER (*stolidly*)

Fat-face.

TOAD

I didn't mean him any more than anyone else. I just murmured the expression to myself. It's a way I have. I'm that sort of person. I murmur things to myself. It's the result of a highly strung temperament and an artistic nature.

USHER

He admits that he passed the expression "fat-face" my lord, and that's good enough for any ordinary jury.

CHIEF WEASEL

Speaking as a special kind of rabbit, I say that it's good enough for me.

MOLE

Weasel!

CHIEF WEASEL

Shut up!

JUDGE

Very well. We have the prisoner condemned out of his own mouth of using most frightful cheek to a member of the rural police. We shall now sentence him severely.

USHER

Wait a bit, my lord. There's that little matter of stealing a valuable motor car without so much as a "with your leave" or a "by your leave."

JUDGE

Does it matter? I mean compared with this unspeakable impertinence to which the prisoner has already confessed?

USHER

Well, it adds more to the sentence, like.

JUDGE

Ah, well, in that case we must certainly go into the matter. Well, Toad, what have you got to say about that?

TOAD

I didn't mean to steal it. It was this way. I was just having a bit of lunch at an inn. I had been very ill, hadn't I, Ratty? And my dear friends Mr. Rat and Mr. Mole and Mr. Badger had been looking after me. It was the first time I'd been up and out, and I was having my bit of lunch, just a round of beef and a few pickled walnuts and a couple of helpings of treacle pudding, when I heard outside "Poop-poop! Poop-poop!"

JUDGE

You heard what?

TOAD (*raptly*)

Poop-poop! Poop-poop!

USHER (*stolidly*)

Imitation of motor car.

JUDGE

Oh! (*To himself*) Poop-poop! Poop-poop! (*Shaking his head*) No, I don't seem to get it.

TOAD

Well, then two gentlemen came in to lunch, and as soon as I'd finished mine, I went out to look at their car. I thought there couldn't be any harm in my only just looking at it. So I looked at it. And then naturally I began to say to myself, "I wonder if this car starts easily." So I wound it up just to see. And then naturally I stepped into the driver's seat, just as I always do, and—and then I saw a policeman with a very fat fa—with a very nice expression, a very handsome policeman; and he said, "You're going a hundred and seventy miles an hour," and I said, "Of course if you say so, dear Mr. Policeman," and then—

JUDGE (*to* USHER)

All this makes it worse, doesn't it?

USHER

Much worse.

JUDGE (*relieved*)

I thought so. It means we can give him a stiffer sentence?

USHER

A much stiffer one.

JUDGE

Good. You were saying, Toad?

BADGER (*rising weightily*)

May I say a few words now, my lord?

JUDGE

Who is this?

USHER

Mr. Badger, a well-known and highly respected member of the community.

JUDGE

So it is, so it is. Well, Mr. Badger?

BADGER

Alack! Alack! O hapless Toad! O ill-fated animal.

JUDGE (*to* USHER)

Is it a recitation?

BADGER

I knew his father, I knew his grandfather, I knew his uncle, the Archdeacon.

JUDGE

This makes it very serious indeed.

BADGER

Many an afternoon have I spent in communion with his

father at Toad Hall, one of the most attractive riverside residences with carriage sweep.

JUDGE

Dear, dear! With carriage sweep, you say.

BADGER

Unhappy day. O feckless Toad. O rash and ill-advised animal! (*He sits down again.*)

JUDGE

Most interesting. We are all indebted to Mr. Badger for his profound and helpful observations. Now, I think, we can proceed to business.

CHIEF WEASEL
Guilty!

JUDGE

Of course he's guilty. That isn't the point. The only difficulty which presents itself in this otherwise very clear case is, how can we possibly make it sufficiently hot for the incorrigible rogue and hardened ruffian whom we see cowering in the Dock before us? Mr. Usher, will you please tell us what is the very stiffest penalty we can impose for each of the three offenses for which the prisoner stands convicted? Without, of course, giving him the benefit of the doubt, because there isn't any.

USHER

Well, my lord, some people would consider that stealing a

valuable motor car was the worst offense, and so it is. But cheeking the police carries the severest penalty, and so it ought. Suppose you were to say a year for the theft, which is mild, and three years for the furious driving, which is lenient, and fifteen years for the cheek, which is purely nominal. Those figures, if added together correctly, tot up to nineteen years.

JUDGE
First-rate!

USHER
So you'd better make it a round twenty and be on the safe side.

TOAD (*meekly*)
I don't mind if it isn't quite round.

JUDGE
Silence! An excellent suggestion, Mr. Usher. Now, prisoner, pull yourself together and try to stand up straight. It's going to be twenty years for you this time. And mind, if you appear before us again, on any charge whatever, we shall have to deal with you very seriously.

CHIEF WEASEL
Hear, hear!

MOLE
Shut up!

JUDGE

Twenty years. Don't forget. Now then, prisoner, before the
rest of us adjourn for lunch, is there anything you would
like to say in the nature of a farewell speech? Any last words
or valedictory utterances?

TOAD (*boldly*)

Yes.

JUDGE (*kindly*)

Well, well, what is it?

TOAD

Fat-face!

JUDGE (*aghast*)

Fat-face? ME?

TOAD (*wildly*)

All of you! All the whole lot of you! All fat-faces! I am
Toad, the Terror of the Highway, Toad, the Traffic-queller,
the Lord of the Lone Trail, before whom all must give way
or be smitten into nothingness and everlasting night. I am
the Toad, the handsome, the popular, the successful Toad.
And what are you? Just fat-faces.

JUDGE

Well, of all the ungrateful things to say.

TOAD

I am the great, the magnificent, the incomprehensible Toad!

RAT (*sadly*)

Oh, Toady, boasting again.

JUDGE

To call me, after all I've done for him, fat-face!

TOAD

The great Toad! (*He breaks into his chant.*)

> The world has held great heroes,
>> As history books have showed;
> But never a name to go down to fame
>> Compared with that of Toad!

JUDGE

Silence!

TOAD

> The clever men at Oxford
>> Know all there is to be knowed,
> But they none of them know one half as much
>> As intelligent Mr. Toad!

JUDGE

Stop him, somebody! Stop him!

TOAD

> The Army all saluted,
>> As they marched along the road;
> Was it the King? or Fat-face?
>> No. It was Mr. Toad!

JUDGE

Take him away! Cast him into the dungeon! Load him with chains! Gag him!

EVERYBODY

Now then. Now then. Better come quietly.

TOAD (*as he is hustled away*)
The Queen and her ladies-in-waiting
　　Sat in the window and sewed:
She cried "Look! who's that handsome man?"
　　They answered "Mr. Toad."

(*His voice is heard more and more faintly in the distance, as he is led to the dungeons.*)

Mr. Toad! Mr. Toad! Mr. Toad!

Scene 2

THE DUNGEON

SCENE. *A Dungeon. On a heap of straw in the corner* TOAD *sleeps uneasily. The door is unlocked and* PHOEBE, *the gaoler's daughter, comes in with breakfast on a tray.* TOAD *sits up and takes the straw from his hair.*

PHOEBE

Good morning, Toad.

TOAD (*gloomily*)

Good morning, woman.

PHOEBE

Slept well?

TOAD

Slept well? How could I sleep well, immured in a dark and noisome dungeon like this?

PHOEBE

Well, some do. See, I've brought your breakfast.

TOAD

Then you will oblige me by taking it away again.

PHOEBE

What, aren't you ever going to eat any more?

TOAD

You don't understand. This is the end.

PHOEBE

You've said that every day for a month past. The end of what?

TOAD

The end of everything. At least it is the end of the career of Toad, which is the same thing. (*He paces up and down.*) The popular and handsome Toad, the rich and hospitable Toad, the Toad so free and careless and debonair.

PHOEBE

Cheer up, there's always hope.

TOAD

Hope? How can I hope ever to be set at large again who have been imprisoned so justly for stealing so handsome a motor car in such an audacious manner, and for such lurid and imaginative cheek bestowed upon such a fat, red-faced policeman?

PHOEBE

Well, there is that, of course.

TOAD

Stupid animal that I was, now I must languish in this dungeon till people who were proud to say they knew me have forgotten the very name of Toad.

PHOEBE

There's no need to languish all the time.

TOAD (*with sobs*)

Oh, wise old Badger. (*To* PHOEBE) A friend of mine. . . . Oh, clever, intelligent Rat and sensible Mole. Two other friends. What sound judgments, what a knowledge of men and matters you possess. Oh, unhappy and forsaken Toad!

PHOEBE (*arranging the breakfast*)

Nice hot buttered toast and tea.

TOAD

Oh, despairing and— Did you say *hot* buttered?

PHOEBE

Made it myself, I did. Father said, "Here's the key of Number 87," he said, "and you can take him his breakfast. He's the most notoriousest dangerous animal in the country," said Father, "and how we shall keep him under lock and key Goodness only knows."

TOAD (*brightening*)

Did he say that?

PHOEBE

His very words. "The most notoriousest dangerous and reckless animal within the four walls of this here castle. And you can take him a couple of old crusts for his breakfast," said Father, "because I must starve and break his indomitable spirit," said Father, "otherwise he'll get the better of me."

TOAD (*his mouth full of it*)
Believe me, girl, I am not ungrateful. You must pay me a visit at Toad Hall one of these days. Drop in to tea one afternoon.

TOAD (*making a great effort to be modest*)
Well, of course, one has one's reputation.

PHOEBE
So I said, "Yes, Father," and as soon as his back was turned I said to myself, "What a shame," and I made this nice buttered toast.

PHOEBE
Is that where you live?

TOAD (*nodding*)
Finest house in these parts for miles around.

PHOEBE
Tell me about it.

TOAD (*proudly*)
Toad Hall is an eligible, self-contained gentleman's residence, very unique, dating in part from the fourteenth century, but replete with every modern convenience. Up-to-date sanitation. Five minutes from church, post office and golf links. Approached by long carriage sweep.

PHOEBE

Fancy! And do your friends, Mr. Badger and Mr. Rat and Mr. Mole, live there with you?

TOAD (*laughing heartily*)

Oh, my dear child! Badger. Rat. Mole. Excellent fellows all, but hardly, how shall I put it, hardly (*With a wave of the paw*) well, hardly. They come to pay me a visit now and then, naturally; always glad to see them; but—well quite frankly, they wouldn't be comfortable at a big house like Toad Hall, not to live. One has to be born to it. Badger lives in a rambling barn of a place nearby; Rat has a little riverside villa; and Mole—well really, I don't know where Mole does live. He's staying with Badger, I fancy, at present. Dear old Badger.

PHOEBE

You're feeling better, aren't you?

TOAD

The artistic temperament. We have our ups and down. (*He returns to his breakfast.*)

PHOEBE (*looking at him thoughtfully*)

Now I wonder.

TOAD (*casually*)

Any prisoners ever been known to escape from this castle of yours?

PHOEBE

Never.

TOAD (*a little dashed*)

Oh! Well, I must see what I can do. I must give my mind to it one day. Excellent buttered toast this.

PHOEBE

I've been giving my mind to it lately.

TOAD

That's the only way to make really good toast.

PHOEBE

I didn't mean to that. I meant to escaping. I think I see a way in which you might do it.

TOAD (*dropping his toast in his excitement*)

You're going to help me?

PHOEBE

Yes. I like you, Toad, and I've felt sorry for you, and for your friends who want to see you again so badly. And I think it's a shame the way you've been treated.

TOAD

They were afraid of me, that's what it was. (*He puffs out his cheeks.*)

PHOEBE

Now listen. I have an aunt who is a washerwoman.

TOAD (*kindly*)

There, there. Never mind. Think no more about it. I have several aunts who ought to be washerwomen.

PHOEBE

Do be quiet a minute, Toad. You talk too much, that's your chief fault. Now my aunt does the washing for all the prisoners in the castle. Naturally we keep anything of that sort in the family. She brings the washing back Friday morning, that's today. Now you're very rich, at least you're always telling me so, and for a few pounds I think I could persuade her to lend you her dress and bonnet and so on, and you could escape as the castle washerwoman. You're very much alike in some ways, particularly about the figure.

TOAD (*indignantly*)

We're not! I have a very elegant figure, for what I am.

PHOEBE

So has my aunt, for what she is. But have it your own way, you horrid proud ungrateful animal, when I'm trying to help you!

TOAD (*quickly*)

Yes, yes, that's all right, thank you very much indeed. But I was only thinking— You surely wouldn't have Mr. Toad of Toad Hall going about the country disguised as a washerwoman?

PHOEBE

All right, then you can stop here as a Toad. I suppose you want to go off in a coach-and-four?

TOAD

No, no! Please! You are a good, kind, clever girl, and I am indeed a proud and stupid Toad. Introduce me to your worthy aunt, if you will be so kind. It would be a privilege to meet her.

PHOEBE

That's better. (*As she goes out*) With a little trouble you'd make quite a nice Toad.

TOAD (*as the door closes*)

Chit!

(*He bursts happily into his song again, as he arranges a little collection of money—notes, gold and silver— on the table, in such a way that it looks like an accident rather than a bribe.* PHOEBE *returns with her* AUNT, *who appears to be dressed in a blanket. She has a bundle of clothes under her arm.*)

PHOEBE

This is Mr. Toad. My aunt.

AUNT

Good morning.

TOAD (*in his Society manner*)

Good morning, dear lady. Charming weather we are having, are we not? Pray sit down. Your niece tells me that you—er—attend to the—er—that is, you have under your charge the habiliments, the more mutable habiliments of the inhabitants of the castle. A delightful profession, I am sure.

AUNT (*stolidly, to* PHOEBE)

Is this the one?

PHOEBE

Yes.

AUNT (*to* TOAD)

I wash.

TOAD

Quite so, quite so.

PHOEBE

I told you the idea, Aunt, didn't I?

AUNT (*eyeing the money*)

Some of it.

(*There is an awkward silence.* PHOEBE *catches* TOAD'S *eye and indicates the money.*)

TOAD

Quite so. (*He clears his throat loudly.*) I was wondering— naturally I shouldn't want to carry all my money about with me. Indeed, in the costume suggested (*He indicates the bundle of clothes.*) I wondered if you would oblige me so far—purely as a favor to me . . .

AUNT

Is that the money?

TOAD (*indicating the money on the table*)

Just a little—er—I haven't counted it—

AUNT

I have.

TOAD

Oh! Well?

AUNT

Here you are. (*She hands over her bundle: cotton print gown, apron, shawl and rusty black bonnet.*)

TOAD (*seizing the bundle*)

My dear lady, I am eternally your debtor. Should you ever find yourself in the neighborhood of Toad Hall, a visit, whether professional or social— (*He holds up the dress.*) Er, how do I . . .

PHOEBE (*much amused*)

I'll help you.

AUNT

You told him the condition?

TOAD

Condition?

PHOEBE

My aunt thinks she ought to be gagged and bound, so as to look as if she had been overcome. You'd like it, too. You wanted to leave the prison in style.

TOAD (*beamingly*)

An excellent idea. So much more in keeping with my character.

AUNT

I brought a bit of rope along, in case like.

TOAD

Splendid!

AUNT (*enjoying it*)

Got a nankerchief?

TOAD (*producing one*)

Yes.

AUNT

Then you gags me first. (*In a hoarse whisper*) Help! Help!
Help! Help! Help!

TOAD (*carried away by the realism of this*)

Silence, woman, else I gag thee.

AUNT (*undeterred*)

Help! Help! Help!

TOAD (*advancing with gag*)

Thou hast brought it on thyself. (*He gags her.*)

AUNT (*pulling down gag*)

A little tighter, I think. Help! Help! Help!

TOAD (*pulling it tighter*)

A murrain on thy cackling tongue! There! (*To* PHOEBE)
Now then, lend a hand with this rope.

PHOEBE

How brave you are! (*She lends a hand.*)

TOAD (*regarding the* AUNT *with pride*)
A neat bit of work that. Now then, how do I get into this?
(*He holds up the dress.*)

PHOEBE

Silly, not like that. Here, give it to me. . . . Now then.
(*She helps* TOAD *in, and does him up.*) Apron. . . . Shawl.
. . . Now the bonnet. There! Well, upon my word, you're
the very living image of her!

(*The* AUNT *makes frantic indications of a desire to
speak.*)

TOAD

What's the matter with her?

PHOEBE

She wants to say something, I think. (*She takes off the gag.*)

AUNT (*with conviction*)
Too ugly.

PHOEBE

Who is?

AUNT

He is.

TOAD

My good woman—

AUNT

Much too ugly. Never do at all.

TOAD (*amazed*)

Really—

AUNT

Not a bit like me. Not good-looking enough.

TOAD

Here give me the gag!

AUNT

Not nearly good-looking enough. Not— (*But she is gagged again.*)

PHOEBE

Now then, Toad, we must hurry. I'll take you to the end of the corridor, and then you go straight down the stairs. You can't mistake the way. And if any of the gaolers stop you and chaff you a bit, because she's very popular, Aunt is—

TOAD (*coldly*)

I shouldn't have thought it.

PHOEBE

Then you must give them a bit of chaff back. But respectable, of course, being a widow woman with a character to lose. Now good-bye and good luck.

TOAD (*nervously*)

Good-bye, good-bye. If you're ever in the neighborhood of Toad Hall . . .

PHOEBE

Which I shan't be. Now, come on, there's a good Toad. You can thank me when you've escaped. Now, don't forget; you're a washerwoman. (*She leads the way out.*)

TOAD

Yes, yes, we must be off. (*Nervously*) I wish I knew a little more what washerwomen talked about. (*In a falsetto voice, as he goes*) I remember once when I was ironing a shirt-front . . .

Scene 3

THE CANAL BANK

SCENE. *Early morning. A quiet spot by the canal bank. The towpath cuts along by the edge of a wood, in which, just here, is a little clearing. At the entrance, half in, half out of a big hollow tree, lies a heap of old clothing, discarded, it would seem, by some washerwoman. It moves. Evidently there is a washerwoman inside it. A voice comes from the interior. No, it is our friend* TOAD.

TOAD (*sleepily*)

I'll wear the light brown suit, and tell the car to be round at eleven o'clock. No, leave the blinds down. (*He sleeps again.*)

(*Two baby rabbits come by with their* MAMA, *on their way to school.*)

FIRST BABY RABBIT (*Harold to the family*)

What's 'at? (*He gazes at* TOAD.)

MAMA RABBIT

Now, now, come along, Harold, you'll be late for school.

SECOND BABY RABBIT (*Lucy*)
What's Harold doing?

HAROLD (*rooted to the hollow tree*)
What is it?

MAMA RABBIT
Never mind now. Just some poor old washerwoman taking a rest. Come along, there's a good boy.

HAROLD
May I play with it?

MAMA RABBIT
Not now, dear.

LUCY
What's Harold saying?

HAROLD
Do washerwomans know tables?

MAMA RABBIT
I expect they do.

LUCY (*proudly*)
I know my twice times. Twice two are four, twice three are six.

HAROLD
What are washerwomans for?

MAMA RABBIT

Now, now, come along. (*She takes his hand.*) Now, Lucy. (*She takes* LUCY's *hand.*) Now let's all run and see how quickly we can go. (*They scamper off.*)

HAROLD (*as they go*)

Why do washerwomans . . . (*But we hear no more.*)

TOAD (*half waking again*)

And tell cook I'll have three eggs this morning, and be sure to give them each four minutes. (*He moves and wriggles, and then slowly sits up.*) There, she's pulled the blinds up, and I told her— Hallo! (*He looks round him in amazement.*) Wherever— (*He stands up, looks at his clothes, looks round him again, and draws a deep breath of happiness.*) Aha! (*He chuckles.*) Toad again! Escaped from prison. Eluded his captors. Evaded his pursuers. The subtle and resourceful Toad! (*He sits down in the sun, and idly removes a few dead leaves from his person.*)

(*A* FOX *comes by, stops, and looks him up and down in a sarcastic sort of way.*)

FOX

Hallo, washerwoman! Half a pair of socks and a pillow-case short this week. Mind it doesn't occur again. (*He goes off sniggering.*)

TOAD

Silly joke! Where's the humor of it? (*He stands up and spreads himself.*) If he had known. If he had only known who it was. Not a common washerwoman, but the great, the good, the entirely glorious Toad! (*He walks round and round in a circle, chanting his song.*)

The world has held great heroes,
    As history books have showed;
But never a name to go down to fame
    Compared with that of Toad.

The animals sat in the Ark and cried,
    Their tears in torrents flowed;
Who was it said "There's land ahead,"
    Encouraging Mr. Toad!

The Queen and her ladies-in-waiting
    Sat in the window and sewed;
She cried "Look, who's that handsome man?"
    They answered, "Mr. Toad."

(*In an ecstasy*) Oh, how clever I am! How clever, how very clever. (*He breaks off suddenly, as voices are heard crying "Toad! Toad! There he is! This way!"*) Oh, misery! Oh, despair! (*Terrified, he rushes into the hollow tree, and burrows under the leaves.*)

(*The* JUDGE, *the* POLICEMAN, *the* USHER *and the* GAOLER *come in.*)

POLICEMAN

This way, your lordship. I heard him singing. All about himself. Just about here it sounded like. (*He begins to look round.*)

JUDGE

Not that revolting song he sang when I had the pleasure of sentencing him to twenty years in a dungeon?

POLICEMAN

That's the song, your lordship. Only he had a new verse to it. Three verses he sang altogether.

JUDGE

As conceited as the old ones?

POLICEMAN

Worse.

JUDGE

Dear, dear. (*To* USHER) What's the penalty for singing conceited songs about yourself? Can I give him another five years?

POLICEMAN

We've got to catch him first.

USHER

Two years a verse is the usual.

JUDGE

Good. Then that's six years. And say ten for having had the ingratitude to escape from a perfectly clean, (*To* GAOLER) ventilated, you said?

GAOLER

Well-ventilated.

JUDGE

Well-ventilated prison. That's another sixteen years. Excellent!

POLICEMAN

We've got to catch him first. But he's about here somewhere, that I do say.

GAOLER

Just look in that hollow tree.

JUDGE

He wouldn't be there, would he? Such a silly place to hide in.

POLICEMAN

Well, you never know. (*He goes to it.* TOAD, *quaking in his fear, displaces the leaves.*) There's something there.

JUDGE

Something undoubtedly. (*They all gather round.*)

USHER

A bird of some sort, most like.

TOAD (*brilliantly*)

Chirp! Chirp! Chirp!

POLICEMAN

Yes, you're right. Only a bird.

JUDGE

Only a bird. What a pity.

USHER

I knew it was only a bird. We're wasting time here.

JUDGE

True. Lead on, policeman.

POLICEMAN

Well, he's not far off. This way. (*They all go off.*)

(*The leaves move again, and then* TOAD's *head peeps cautiously out.*)

TOAD (*panting with fear*)

Oh my! What an ass I am. What a conceited and heedless ass. Swaggering again. Shouting and singing songs again. Sitting about and gassing again. Oh my! (*He stands up and looks round cautiously, then explores the clearing. The pursuit has died away.*) Ah! That was good! Just a little resource, a little cleverness! "Only a bird." Ha, ha, ha! That will amuse the dear old Badger. I can hear his hearty laugh. "We're wasting time here." How the dear fellow, Mole, will enjoy that! "I knew it was only a bird." The good Rat will chuckle when I tell him.

(*He is standing with his back to the towpath. A horse, dragging a towrope, comes along the path, stops, and puts his head ingratiatingly over* TOAD's *shoulder.* TOAD's *jaw drops. His knees tremble.*)

TOAD (*terrified*)

All right. I'll come quietly. (*He looks nervously round, sees the horse, and gives a sob of relief.*) You quite startled me! I thought it was—I said I'd come quietly, just to put him off his guard. That was all. Just to— Hallo! (*He sees the rope.*) A barge. Aha! I will hail the owner and pitch him a yarn and he will give me a lift by a route which is not troubled by fat policemen. Perhaps (*He heaves a sigh.*) I may even get some breakfast.

(*The horse has stopped and is cropping the grass. Evidently he is meant to stop here, for a comfortable-looking barge-woman comes in, carrying a bag of corn.*)

BARGE-WOMAN

A nice morning, ma'am.

TOAD

The same to you, ma'am.

BARGE-WOMAN (*holding up bag*)

Give the horse a bit of breakfast.

TOAD (*with meaning*)

The horse?

BARGE-WOMAN

Had mine. (*She ties the bag on to the horse's head.*)

TOAD

And a good hearty breakfast I'm sure it was, ma'am.

BARGE-WOMAN

Well, I won't deny I like my vittals.

TOAD

You're right, ma'am, you're right. (*Casually*) And finished it all up, I daresay. Fried ham and eggs and all of it.

BARGE-WOMAN (*with a laugh*)

Pretty well, ma'am, pretty well.

TOAD

Ah. (*He is gloomily silent.*)

BARGE-WOMAN (*having finished with the horse*)

You seem in trouble, ma'am.

TOAD

Trouble! Here's my married daughter she sends off to me to come at once. So off I comes, not knowing what may be happening, but fearing the worst, as you'll understand if you happen to be a mother too, ma'am. And I've left my business to look after itself. I'm in the washing and laundering line, as you can see, ma'am; and I've left my breakfast, I was that upset, and I've lost all my money and lost my way and lost my breakfast, as you might say, too. And as for my married daughter—well, you know what it is, ma'am, being a married woman yourself, I daresay.

BARGE-WOMAN

Dear, dear. Where might your married daughter be living?

TOAD

Toad Hall, ma'am. The finest house in these parts, as no doubt you've heard tell. Tudor and Jacobean, my daughter tells me, with ornamental boathouse. That is, she lives just close to it.

BARGE-WOMAN

Toad Hall? Why, I'm going that way myself. You come along in the barge with me and I'll give you a lift.

TOAD

I'm sure you're very kind, ma'am.

BARGE-WOMAN

Don't mention it. So you're in the washing business. And a fine business you've got too, I daresay, if I'm not making too free in saying so.

TOAD

Finest business in the whole country! All the gentry come to me. Washing, ironing, clear starching, making up gents' fine shirts for evening wear—all done under my own eye.

BARGE-WOMAN

But surely you don't do it all yourself, ma'am?

TOAD

Oh, I have girls, twenty or thirty of them always at work. But you know what girls are, ma'am. Idle trollops, that's what I call them.

BARGE-WOMAN

They are that. And are you very fond of washing?

TOAD

I love it. I simply dote on it. Never so happy as when I've got both arms in the washtub.

BARGE-WOMAN

What a bit of luck meeting you!

TOAD (*nervously*)

Why, what do you mean?

BARGE-WOMAN

Well, look at me. I like washing too, same as you. But there's my husband, who ought by rights to be here now, steering or looking after the horse. He has gone off with the dog to see if he can't pick up a rabbit for dinner somewhere. Says he'll catch us up at the next lock. Meantime, how am I to get on with my washing?

TOAD

Oh, never mind about the washing. Try and fix your mind on that rabbit. Got any onions?

BARGE-WOMAN

It's no good, I keep thinking of that washing. And if it's a pleasure to you to do it, as you say, being that fond of it, why then—

TOAD (*hastily*)

No, no, I mustn't deprive you, not after you've been looking forward to it for weeks, as I expect you have. I'll steer, and then you can get on with your washing in your own way. The fact is, I am more used to gentlemen's things myself; shirt-fronts and cuffs, dressy things, if you know what I mean. It's my special line.

BARGE-WOMAN

I daresay the other would come just as easy to you once you began. Besides, it takes some practice to steer a barge properly when you've never done it before.

TOAD

Never done it before? Why, ma'am, it's my one recreation, after wash hours. First thing I do, as soon as I can get away, is to go down to the canal for a bit of barge-steering. It's got hold of me, my friends say, almost like a disease. Fact is, it's always been in the family. My father owned twenty or thirty barges, big ones, never less than three horses pulling them. Great big enormous ones.

BARGE-WOMAN (*with suspicion*)

I don't believe you're a washerwoman at all.

TOAD (*indignantly*)

Of course I'm a washerwoman! Should I be likely to say I was a washerwoman, if I wasn't? It isn't a thing you want to go about saying, if you aren't. Why should I be wearing a washerwoman's clothes if I'm not a washerwoman?

BARGE-WOMAN (*firmly*)

Well, if you ask me, ma'am, I should say it's all a piece of deceit. I don't go for to say what you're doing it for, but what I do say is that I won't have deceit on my barge. And that's for you, ma'am. (*She goes to untie the bag from the horse's head.*)

    TOAD (*with dignity*)
Oh, indeed, ma'am.

    BARGE-WOMAN
And I say this, ma'am, that if you have a daughter, which I daresay you haven't, I'm sorry for her, having a mother which practices deceit. (*She comes away with the bag.*) And I'll wish you good morning, ma'am. (*She goes out, nose in air.*)

    TOAD (*shouting after her*)
You common, low, fat, barge-woman, don't you dare to talk to your betters like that. Washerwoman, indeed! I would have you know that I am the Toad, the Terror of the Countryside, the Scourge of Barge-women! Keep your stupid little barge! I prefer—riding! (*He unfastens the tow-rope, jumps on the horse's back and gallops off.*) The Toad! The Toad!

    BARGE-WOMAN (*rushing after him*)
Help! Help! The notorious Toad! Help!

    (*The* POLICEMAN *and the others join in the pursuit.*)

    ALL
The Toad! The Toad!

ACT IV

Scene 1

RAT'S HOUSE BY THE RIVER

SCENE. RAT'S *riverside residence. In construction it is something like the cabin of a ship. Through the large portholes at the back, the opposite bank of the river can be seen.* RAT *is busy with a large heap of pistols, swords and cudgels.*

At one of the portholes the head of the TOAD, *still wearing his washerwoman's bonnet over one eye, appears suddenly.*

TOAD (*from outside*)
Help! Help!

RAT (*thoughtfully listening*)
Funny. That sounded like Toad's voice.

TOAD
Help!

RAT
Yes, if Toad had been anywhere but where he is, poor un-

fortunate animal, I should have said—(*He comes into* TOAD's *line of sight.*)

TOAD

Help! Help!

RAT (*turning round*)

It is! Toady! However—

TOAD

Give us a hand, Rat. I'm about done.

RAT (*excitedly*)

Old Toad! (*He seizes hold of him.*) Well, this is— What's the matter? No strength left? I know. But however—

TOAD

You'll have to pull me in. I'm about done.

RAT

That's all right. Got one kick left in you? Good. Well, when I say, "Kick," kick, and I'll pull, and— Now then, ready?

TOAD (*faintly*)

Yes.

RAT

Then kick! (TOAD *kicks.* RAT *pulls, and he tumbles in on to the floor.*) There!

TOAD (*gasping*)

Oh! Oh! Oh!

RAT (*helping him up*)

Come on the sofa a bit, won't you?

TOAD (*faintly*)

Thank you, dear Ratty, thank you. (*He flops onto the sofa.*)

RAT

Here, drink this. You're about done. (*He hands* TOAD *a bottle.*)

TOAD (*drinking*)

Ah! (*He drinks again.*) That's better. I shall soon be all right. A passing faintness.

RAT (*looking at him*)

Poor old Toady. And wet as wet. . . . And am I wrong, or are you disguised in parts as a washerwoman who has seen better days?

TOAD (*complacently*)

Aha.

RAT

That's more like you. Escaped, eh? In disguise?

TOAD (*more complacently*)

Aha. (*He begins to sit up and take notice.*)

RAT

That's much better. We'll soon have you all right.

TOAD

It takes a good deal to put me out, Ratty. Just a passing faintness which might happen to anyone who had been through what I've been through.

RAT

You've been through a lot, I expect.

TOAD

My dear Ratty, the times I've been through since I saw you last, you simply can't think!

RAT

Yes. Well, when you've got those horrible things off, and cleaned yourself up a bit—

TOAD

The times! Such trials, such sufferings, and all so nobly borne!

RAT

You'll find some dry clothes upstairs.

TOAD

Such escapes, such disguises, such subterfuges, and all so cleverly planned and carried out!

RAT

Quite so. Well—

TOAD

Been in prison, got out of it, of course. Stole a horse, rode away on it. Humbugged everybody, made 'em do exactly as I wanted. Oh, I *am* a smart Toad, and no mistake. Now what do you think my very last exploit was?

RAT (*severely*)

I don't know, Toad. But seeing where it was I found you, and the state you were in, I should say that somebody had dropped you into the river, and then thrown mud at you. It isn't a thing to boast about, really it isn't, Toad.

TOAD

Pooh, that was nothing. I just happened to be—to be heading a pursuit on my horse, right in front of everybody else, in my usual way. And accidentally, not noticing the river in the enthusiasm of the chase, and the horse stopping a moment or two before I did—

RAT (*warningly*)

Toad.

TOAD

But I wasn't going to tell you about that. Now what do you think—

RAT (*taking him by the shoulders*)

Toad!

TOAD

Here, hold on a moment. I just want to tell you—

RAT

Toad, you will go upstairs at once, and see if you can possibly make yourself look like a respectable animal again, for a more shabby, bedraggled, disreputable-looking object than you are now, I never set eyes on.

TOAD (*with dignity*)
You can hardly realize, Ratty, to whom you are—

RAT
Now stop swaggering and arguing and be off. Badger and Mole will be in directly.

TOAD (*airily*)
Oh, ah! Yes, of course, the Mole and the Badger. What's become of them, the dear fellows? I had forgotten all about them.

RAT (*gravely*)
Well may you ask!

TOAD
Why, what—

RAT
You will hear in good time. Badger himself may prefer to break the news to you. Be off now, and prepare yourself. Why, what's the matter?

TOAD (*who has wandered in front of a mirror and is regarding himself with horror*)
Is this glass of yours all right?

RAT

Of course. Why?

TOAD

I hoped— You see, it's the first time I— You're quite right,
Ratty. Nobody could carry off a costume like this. (*Meekly*)
I'll go and change. (*He goes out.*)

> (RAT, *left alone, fetches duster, pan and brush, and be-
> gins to clean up after* TOAD, *murmuring, "Dear, dear!"
> to himself, and "Well, I never!" While he is so en-
> gaged,* BADGER *and* MOLE *come in.*)

RAT (*eagerly*)

Hallo, here you are! I say, what do you think?

MOLE (*dropping into a chair*)

Too tired to think, Ratty, and that's a fact.

RAT

Yes, but—

BADGER (*gruffly*)

Nobody thinks nowadays. That's the trouble. Too much
action, not enough thought. (*He stretches himself on the
sofa.*)

RAT

Yes, but—

MOLE (*to* RAT)

He's a bit low, just now. We've had a hard day. He'll be
all right directly.

RAT

Yes, but what do you think? Toad's back.

MOLE (*jumping up*)

Toad! Back where?

RAT

Here!

MOLE

Where?

RAT (*with a jerk of the head*)

Cleaning. You ought to have seen him, Mole. He'd have made you laugh.

BADGER (*with his eyes shut*)

Unhappy animal.

MOLE

Escaped?

RAT (*nodding*)

'Mmm. So he says. But you know what Toad is.

BADGER

I knew his father. Ah me!

MOLE

Has he heard the news?

RAT

Not yet. I said Badger would tell him.

MOLE

Old Toad! . . . He's just in time. Badger thinks it will be tonight!

RAT (*eagerly*)

Not really?

MOLE

Yes. He says so.

RAT

I've been polishing up the pistols and cutlasses. They're all ready.

MOLE

Good. We shall want all we can.

BADGER (*solemnly rousing himself*)

Rat.

RAT (*turning round*)

Hallo?

BADGER

Did I hear you say that our young friend Toad had escaped from his noisome dungeon?

RAT

Came in five minutes ago. In such a state.

BADGER

I would speak with him.

RAT

He's just having a wash.

BADGER (*severely*)

This is no time for washing. We have work before us to-night. Hard fighting. Washing can wait. Where do you think I should have been if, at the crisis of my life, I had stopped to wash? Where would my revered father have been, if he had put soap before strategy? Where would my beloved grandfather—

MOLE (*loudly*)

Toady!

TOAD (*from outside*)

Hallo, Mole, old fellow!

BADGER

Thank you, Mole. (*He closes his eyes again.*)

MOLE (*to* RAT)

I heard all about his beloved grandfather this morning. Most interesting.

(TOAD *comes in, almost his old self.*)

TOAD (*cheerily*)

Hallo, you fellows!

MOLE (*delightedly*)

Toady!

BADGER (*solemnly rising*)

Welcome home, Toad. Alas! what am I saying? Home, indeed. This is a poor homecoming. Unhappy Toad. (*He sinks on to the sofa again.*)

MOLE

Fancy having you back! And today of all days. To think that you have escaped from prison, you clever, intelligent Toad.

TOAD

Clever? Oh, no. I'm not clever, really. Badger doesn't think so. Rat doesn't think so. I've only broken out of the strongest prison in England, that's all. And disguised myself, and gone about the country on my horse humbugging everybody, that's all. Clever? Oh dear no.

RAT

Oh, Toady!

TOAD

Well, I shall be strolling along to Toad Hall. One does get appreciated at home. Mole, if you like to drop in to coffee one evening, and care to hear a few of my milder adventures—

MOLE (*sadly*)

Oh, Toady, and you haven't heard.

TOAD

Heard what? Quick, don't spare me! What haven't I heard?

MOLE

The Stoats and the Weasels!

RAT

The Wild Wooders!

MOLE

And how they've been and gone—

RAT

And taken Toad Hall.

MOLE

And been living there ever since.

RAT

Going on simply anyhow.

MOLE

Lying in bed half the day.

RAT

Breakfast at all hours.

MOLE

Eating your grub and drinking your drink.

RAT

And making bad jokes about you, and singing vulgar songs.

MOLE

About . . . (*He hesitates.*)

RAT

About . . . (*He hesitates.*)

MOLE

Well, about prisons and magistrates and policemen.

RAT

Horrid personal songs with no humor in them.

MOLE

That's what's happened, Toad. And it's no good pretending it hasn't.

RAT

And they're all telling everybody that they've come to Toad Hall to stay for good.

TOAD

Oh, have they! I'll jolly soon see about that!

RAT

Yes, but how?

TOAD (*doubtfully*)

Well—well—well, what I shall do . . .

RAT

Of course, what you ought to do . . .

MOLE

No, he oughtn't. Nothing of the sort. What he ought to do is, he ought to . . .

TOAD

Well, I shan't do it anyhow. I've been ordered about quite enough. It's my house we're talking about, and I know exactly what to do, and I'll tell you. I'm going to—

BADGER

Be quiet, all of you! (*They are silent.*) Toad!

TOAD (*meekly*)

Yes, Badger?

BADGER

When you got into trouble a short time ago, and brought disgrace upon your own name, and shame and sorrow upon your friends, I resolved that on your return from your enforced seclusion, I would take the first opportunity of pointing out to you the folly of your ways.

TOAD (*meekly*)

Yes, Badger. Thank you, Badger.

BADGER

I even went so far as to jot down a few rough notes on the subject. Where are they, Rat?

RAT (*handing him a sheet of paper*)

Here you are.

BADGER

Thank you. (*Reading*) "To make suet dumplings" . . .

RAT

It's the other side.

BADGER

Ah yes, here we are.

TOAD (*meekly*)

I'd rather have the bit about the dumplings, if it's all the same to you.

BADGER (*reading*)

"(1) Conceit and its consequence. (2) Reverend Uncle, grief of. (3) Toad, whither tending?" (*He puts the paper down.*) But the moment for all this is past.

TOAD (*humbly*)

Just as you like, Badger old man.

BADGER

The moment is past, because it is obvious now to everybody here where your folly has brought you. Toad Hall is in the hands of your enemies. Sentries guard it day and night. Unhappy Toad.

TOAD (*bursting into tears*)

Alas, alas! Toad Hall, that desirable riverside residence, in the hands of Stoats and Weasels! This is, indeed, the end of everything! (*He rolls onto the sofa in his grief.*)

BADGER

Not quite the end. I haven't said my last word yet. Now I'm going to tell you a great secret. We are too few to attack from the front, but there is an underground passage that leads from the River Bank right up into the middle of Toad Hall.

TOAD (*sitting up brightly*)

Oh, nonsense, Badger! I know every inch of Toad Hall inside and out. You've been listening to gossip, that's what you've been doing.

BADGER (*severely*)

Right up into the middle of Toad Hall. When your father, who was a particular friend of mine, told me about it, he said, "Don't tell my son. He means well," he said, "but he's very light and irresponsible in character," he said, "and simply cannot hold his tongue. If he's ever in a real fix," he said, "and it would be of use to him," he said, "you may tell him. But not before." That's what he said, Toad. Knowing the sort of animal you were.

TOAD

Well, well, perhaps I am a bit of a talker. A popular fellow such as I am, my friends get round me, we chaff, we sparkle, we tell witty stories and somehow my tongue gets wagging. I have the gift of conversation. I have been told that I ought to have a *salon*, whatever that may be.

BADGER (*severely*)

At present, my young friend, you haven't even got a box-room.

TOAD (*sweetly*)

How true, dear Badger, and how well put. But you have a plan in that wise old head of yours. This passage. How shall we use it?

BADGER

Tonight the Chief Weasel is giving a banquet. It's his birthday. While they are all feasting, careless of the morrow, we four, armed to the teeth, will creep silently, by way of the passage, into the butler's pantry.

TOAD

Ah! that squeaky board in the butler's pantry!

BADGER

Armed to the teeth, you and Rat, by one door—

RAT (*looking up*)

Yes, Badger.

BADGER

And me and Mole by the other—

MOLE

Yes, Badger.

BADGER

Also armed to the teeth—we shall—

MOLE

Creep out of the pantry—

RAT

With our pistols, and swords and sticks—

BADGER

And rush in on them—

TOAD (*ecstatically*)

And whack 'em and whack 'em and whack 'em.

BADGER

Exactly. (*He pats* TOAD *on the back.*) You have caught the spirit of it perfectly. Good Toad!

TOAD

I'll learn 'em to steal my house.

RAT

Teach 'em, Toad, not learn 'em.

BADGER

But we don't want to teach 'em. Toad's quite right. We want to learn 'em, and, what's more, we're going to. Now then, to rest, all of you. We start at 9 o'clock, and we must be fresh for it. (*He settles down on the sofa.*)

RAT

I'll just get the lanterns trimmed. (*He goes out.*)

MOLE (*settling down in a chair*)

Badger's right. I want a rest.

TOAD (*drawing a chair next to* MOLE)
Yes, we must rest.

(*He begins to chuckle.* MOLE, *eyes closed, takes no notice.* TOAD *glances at him and chuckles more loudly.* MOLE *lazily opens an eye.*)

MOLE (*sleepily*)
Eh?

TOAD (*laughing heartily*)
I was just thinking; most amusing thing, really rather funny. I was in a hollow tree and a policeman, well, a whole army of 'em, was looking for me. And one of 'em said, "Is that a bird?" Ha, ha, ha! Really very funny. "Is that a bird or what?" And what do you think I did? Ha, ha, ha! I said . . . (*and so on.* MOLE *sleeps.*)

Scene 2

THE UNDERGROUND PASSAGE

SCENE. *The Secret Passage. The four conspirators steal in—*BADGER, RAT, MOLE, TOAD. BADGER *and* MOLE *carry the lanterns. They are all armed to the teeth.*

BADGER (*to* RAT)

H'sh!

RAT (*to* MOLE)

H'sh!

MOLE (*to* TOAD)

H'sh!

TOAD (*loudly*)

What?

THE OTHERS

H'sh!

TOAD

Oh, all right.

BADGER

We are now in the secret passage, but not yet under the

house. For the moment silence is not absolutely necessary,
but later on . . .

TOAD (*airily*)
Quite so, quite so.

BADGER
Now, it's all understood? Mole and I burst into the banqueting hall by the east door, and drive them towards the
west door, where Rat and Toad—

TOAD (*impatiently*)
That's all right, Badger. Let's get at 'em.

BADGER
Rat, you're responsible for the operations on the western
front. You understand? What's the matter?

RAT (*who is trying to read something by the light of*
MOLE's *lantern*)

Just before we start, hadn't we better make sure we've
got everything? (*Reading*) One belt, one sword, one cut-
lass, one cudgel, one pair of pistols, one policeman's trun-
cheon, one policeman's whistle— (TOAD *blows his loudly.*)

BADGER (*alarmed*)
What's that?

MOLE (*reproachfully*)
Toad!

BADGER (*sternly*)
Was that you, Toad?

TOAD (*meekly*)
I just wanted to be sure it worked.

BADGER
Now, Toad, I warn you solemnly, if I have any trouble from you, you'll be sent back, as sure as fate.

TOAD (*humbly*)
Oh, Badger.

BADGER
Well, I warn you.

RAT
One policeman's whistle, two pairs of handcuffs, bandages, sticking plaster, flask, sandwich case. Now, has everybody got that?

BADGER (*with a laugh*)
I've got it, but I'm going to do all I want to do with this here stick.

RAT
It's just as you like, Badger. It's only that I don't want you to blame me afterwards and say that I'd forgotten anything.

BADGER

Well, well! But no pistols, unless we have to. We shall only be shooting each other.

RAT

Pistols in reserve, of course. Eh, Moly?

MOLE

Of course. Eh, Toad?

TOAD (*who is examining his*)

Of course. (*It goes off with a tremendous bang. Everybody jumps.*)

MOLE (*reproachfully*)

Toad!

BADGER

Toad? You don't mean to say that that was Toad again? After what I've just said?

TOAD

I—I just—I didn't . . .

BADGER

Very well then, you go back.

TOAD (*falling on his knees*)

Oh, please, Badger, please!

BADGER

No! I can't take the risk.

TOAD

Oh, Badger, please. After all I've been through, and my own house too. You mustn't send me back.

BADGER (*wavering*)

I ought to.

MOLE

Look here, I'll go last and keep an eye on him.

RAT

And we'll take his pistols and his whistle away. (*He does so.*)

BADGER

Well . . .

RAT

We'll leave 'em here, see. (*He puts them on the ground.*) Just here. It might be very useful, if we had to beat a retreat, to find a couple of freshly primed pistols and a policeman's whistle to fall back on. That'll be all right, Badger.

BADGER (*gruffly*)

Very well. (*He leads on.*) Now then, no more talking. From this moment absolute silence.

TOAD (*very humbly*)

Just before we begin the silence, Badger . . .

BADGER (*after waiting in silence*)
Well, what is it?

TOAD
A-a-a-a—tishoo! That's all. I felt it coming. Now I won't
say another word.
(*They pass on.*)

Scene 3

THE BANQUETING ROOM
IN TOAD HALL

SCENE. *The banqueting room, a magnificent apartment in Toad Hall. It being the* CHIEF WEASEL'S *birthday, a banquet is in progress. The hero of the occasion, a laurel wreath on his brow, sits at the head of the main table, his admirers round him. Pressed for a few more words, he rises.*

CHIEF WEASEL

Friends and Fellow Animals. Before we part this evening I have one final toast to propose. (*Hear, hear!*) It is a toast which on all occasions has something of solemnity in it, something even of sadness, but never more so than on this occasion. Absent Friends. (*Hear, hear!*) Absent Friends. With this toast I couple first the name of our kind host, Mr. Toad. (*Loud laughter*) Although unable to be present himself tonight (*Laughter*) owing to a previous engagement (*Laughter*) Mr. Toad has generously put his entire establishment at our disposal for as long as we like to make use of it. (*Loud laughter*) We all know Toad—(*Hear, hear!*) good Toad, wise Toad, modest Toad. (*Laughter*) It is a personal sorrow to every one of us that he is not amongst us tonight. Let me sing you a little song which I have composed on this subject. (*Hear, hear!*)

Toad he went a pleasuring
  Gaily down the road.
They put him in prison for twenty years:
  Poor old Toad!

Toad he had a beautiful house,
  A most refined abode.
They put him in prison for twenty years:
  Poor old Toad!

Toad he had much money and goods
  All carefully bestowed.
They put him in prison for twenty years:
  Poor old Toad!

CHIEF WEASEL

Chorus, please

  Poor old Toad!
  Poor old Toad!
  They put him in prison for twenty years:
  Poor old Toad!

(*Loud applause*)

CHIEF WEASEL

But while we are thinking of our good host, Mr. Toad, we must not forget our other absent friends, Mr. Badger, Mr. Rat and Mr. Mole. (*Laughter*) it is a particular sorrow to me that they are not with us tonight, living as they do, unlike Mr. Toad, so very conveniently in the neighborhood. From time to time, indeed, of late, we have caught glimpses of them, behind hedges. (*Laughter*) We have seen their back views (*Laughter*) in the distance (*Laughter*) running away. (*Laughter*) We know that they cannot plead absence from the country as an excuse for their absence from our board, so that the only reason for it must be excessive shyness. (*Laughter*) Modesty. (*Laughter*) All the more do we regret that they did not see fit to join us. Fellow animals, I give you the toast, Absent Friends!

ALL (*rising and drinking*)
Absent Friends!

A DEEP VOICE OUTSIDE
Absent Friends!

ALL (*to each other*)
What's that? . . . What is it? . . . I didn't hear anything. . . . Nonsense. . . .

(*The door opens.* BADGER *and* MOLE *rush in.*)

BADGER (*his war-cry*)
Up the Badger!

MOLE (*his*)
A Mole! A Mole!

BADGER (*wielding his cudgel*)
Lay on to 'em, boys.

MOLE (*between blows*)

Sorry we're late, Weasel (*Biff!*) but many thanks all the same (*Biff!*) for the kind invitation (*Biff!*)

CHIEF WEASEL

The other door. Quick!

(*The other door opens, and* TOAD *and* RAT *charge in.*)

TOAD (*terribly*)

I've come home, Weasel. (*He makes for him.*) How are you? (*Bang!*) Toad he went a-pleasuring, did he! (*Bang!*) I'll pleasure you! (*Bang!*)

THE ENEMY (*variously*)

Help! . . . Mercy! . . . All right, all right! . . . I say, shut up!

BADGER

Wallop 'em, boys. Keep walloping!

(*Some of the enemy are showing fight, some are escaping through the doors and windows, some are begging for mercy with uplifted paws.*)

RAT (*to one of the weaker brethren*)

Surrender, do you? All right. Get in that corner there.

(*There is a small rush for "that corner there."*)

MOLE (*seeking whom he can devour*)

A Mole! A Mole! (*To an unhappy Stoat*) Hallo, were you

looking for anything? (*Biff!*) Just wanted to say good-bye?
(*Biff!*) Good-bye! (*Biff!*) Sorry you can't stop. (*He biffs
him out of the door.*)

TOAD (*to a terrified Ferret*)
Good evening! Do you sing at all?

FERRET
N-no, sir, please, sir.

TOAD
Not just a little song?

FERRET
N-no, sir. I—I never l-learnt singing.

TOAD (*swinging his club*)
Not just a funny little song about a poor old Toad?

FERRET (*with an effort*)
N-no, sir.

TOAD (*ingratiatingly*)
Try.

FERRET (*foolishly—in a high squeaky voice*)
Poor old Toad!

TOAD (*furiously*)
I'll learn you to sing!

(*With a squeal the* FERRET *scurries into* RAT's *corner.*)

RAT (*getting in front of* TOAD)

All prisoners here, Toad. I'm looking after them. (*He walks up and down in front of them, pistol in hand.*)

BADGER (*walloping the last of the others out of the window*)

There! That's the lot! (*He wipes his brow.*) A pity. I was just beginning to enjoy it. What about your little party, Rat?

RAT

They've surrendered. I thought they might come in useful, waiting on us and so on.

BADGER

If any of 'em wants to go on for a bit longer . . .

CHORUS

No, sir, please, sir.

BADGER

Ah! (*He looks round the room.* TOAD *is conducting an imaginary battle with a particularly stubborn adversary.*)

TOAD (*getting his blow in*)

Aha! (*Dodging an imaginary one*) That's no good. (*Getting another in*) More like that!

BADGER

Hallo! (TOAD, *recalled to himself, breaks off the engagement rather sheepishly.*) Now then, Toad, stir your stumps, and look lively. I want some grub, I do. We've got your house back for you, and you don't offer us so much as a sandwich.

RAT

Just a moment, Badger. What about the sentries?

BADGER

Sentries, yes.

RAT

They may be still at their posts.

TOAD

Sentries, pooh! They've run away far enough by now, haven't they, Mole?

MOLE

If they're wise they have.

RAT

I think it would be safer if Mole and I just . . .

BADGER

Sensible Rat. There spoke the voice of wisdom. (*Picking up his cudgel*) You and I and Mole—

RAT

Don't you bother, Badger. Mole and I—

BADGER (*grimly*)

When I go walloping I go walloping.

TOAD

So do I. Come on, I'll lead the way.

BADGER

You will do nothing of the sort, Toad. You've asked us to stay to supper and we're staying to supper. Well, where is the supper? If this isn't your house, say so, and Mole can entertain us.

RAT (*indicating the prisoners*)
They'll help you get it ready, Toady.

TOAD (*reluctantly*)
Oh, all right.

MOLE (*to* TOAD, *as the others go out*)
Don't forget the wine, Toad. We shall want to drink your health, and you'll have to make a speech.

TOAD (*cheering up*)
Oh, right, right. That's all right, leave that to me.

(MOLE *goes out.* TOAD *is left with the now penitent prisoners, about eight of the smaller Stoats and Ferrets.*)

TOAD (*to his slaves*)
Now then, bustle up! (*They bustle up eagerly.*)

CHORUS

Yes, sir, coming, sir!

TOAD

Get busy.

CHORUS

Yes, sir, please, sir!

TOAD

I owe you a leathering apiece as it is.

CHORUS

Please, sir, no, sir!

TOAD

Well, get busy, and perhaps I won't say any more about it.

(*They are very busy and the hall begins to look tidy again.*)

TOAD (*sitting down at the head of the table*)

Got a pencil any of you?

ONE OF THEM

Yes, sir.

TOAD (*taking it*)

Thanks. All right, don't hang about, get busy. (*He takes a piece of paper from his pocket and begins to write.*)

THE PRISONERS (*whispering to each other*)

He's writing. . . . He's writing a letter. . . . It isn't a letter. . . . It's my pencil he's using. . . . I wonder who

he's writing to. . . . Shall we ask him what he's writing?
. . . I will if you will. . . . You ask him, it's your pencil.
. . . No, you . . . all right, I don't mind. . . . Well, go
on then.

THE BRAVE ONE
Please, sir.

TOAD (*proudly*)
There!

THE BRAVE ONE
Please, sir.

TOAD
Now, I daresay all you young fellows are wondering what
I've been doing?

CHORUS
Please, sir, yes, sir.

TOAD
Well, I've just been jotting down a few rough notes.

CHORUS
Oo, sir.

TOAD
Just a few notes for a little entertainment I have sketched
out, a little informal sing-song or *conversazione* to celebrate
my return.

CHORUS

Yes, sir, thank you, sir.

TOAD

Something like this:

(1) Speech. By Toad.

And then I make a note. "There will be other speeches by Toad during the evening." Just so as to reassure people.

CHORUS

Yes, sir.

TOAD

(2) Address. By Toad.

Synopsis. You all know what that means, of course?

CHORUS

Please, sir, no, sir.

TOAD

Well, it just means—well, you'll see what it means directly. It's just a sort of synopsis.

CHORUS

Yes, sir.

TOAD

Synopsis. Our Prison System. The Art of Disguise. Barge Life. Steeple-chasing and its dangers. A Typical English Squire.

CHORUS

Yes, sir.

TOAD

(3) Imitations of Various Bird Notes. By Toad.

(4) Song. By Toad. (Composed by Himself.)

(5) Other compositions by Toad. (Sung by the Composer.)

(6) Song. "For He's a Jolly Good Fellow." (Sung by Badger, Rat and Mole.)

CHORUS

Oo, sir.

TOAD

That's all, just a few rough notes. Of course it may shape a little differently as the evening goes on. There are one or two conjuring tricks which I used to know, something to do with three billiard balls and a globe of goldfish. They may come back to me or they may not. We shall see.

CHORUS

Yes, sir, thank you, sir.

THE BRAVE ONE

Could you give us the song now, sir?

TOAD (*pleased*)

Give it you now, eh?

CHORUS

Oo, please, sir.

TOAD

Well, well. (*He gets up and walks to the middle of the room.*)

THE BRAVE ONE (*picking up the* CHIEF WEASEL'S *wreath*)
Wouldn't you like to wear this, sir?

TOAD

You think—eh? Well, perhaps you're right. (*He puts it on.*)

CHORUS
Oo, sir!

TOAD
Suits me, eh?

CHORUS
Please, sir, yes, sir.

TOAD

Some people can wear 'em and some can't. You have the manner or you haven't. There it is. You can't explain it.

CHORUS
Yes, sir. Where will you stand, sir?

THE BRAVE ONE (*bringing a stool*)
Won't you stand on this, sir?

TOAD (*modestly mounting*)
Well, perhaps . . .

CHORUS

Oo, sir!

TOAD

Now this is just a little song, and it's called "When the Toad Came Home."

CHORUS

Yes, sir.

TOAD

There's only one verse at present, but it can be sung any number of times.

THE BRAVE ONE

Yes, sir. May we all sing it?

TOAD

Certainly, certainly. It is really composed with the idea of being sung by a great many people.

CHORUS

Yes, sir. (*They group themselves round him, expectantly.*)

TOAD (*solemnly*)

"When the Toad Came Home."

(*Singing*)

   The Toad came home!

There was panic in the parlor, there was howling in the hall,

There was crying in the cowshed and a snorting in the stall,
There was smashing in of window, there was crashing in
of door,
There was bashing of the enemy who fainted on the floor,
When the Toad came home!

(*All the prisoners dance in a circle round* TOAD, *singing this song.* TOAD *stands wreathed above them, raptly enjoying it. In the middle of the second verse* BADGER, RAT *and* MOLE *return.*)

BADGER (*appalled*)
Toad! Get down at once!

(TOAD *does not hear him. He is far away. The singers finish their verse but go on dancing round the hero.*)

MOLE (*reproachfully*)
Toady!

RAT (*to* BADGER)
It's no good. I know him. He's practically in a trance. Let him have his evening out.

MOLE
We'll talk to him in the morning.

RAT
Talking's no good to Toad. He'll always come back to what he is.

BADGER (*grimly*)

All the same, I'll talk to him.

RAT

But let him have his hour first.

BADGER

Oh, all right.

(*They stand watching. The dancers are singing again now.*)

MOLE (*apologetically*)

You know, there's something about that tune. It's only just . . . I shan't be . . . (*And suddenly he is in the circle, dancing and singing.*)

BADGER

He's very young still, is Mole.

RAT

Y-yes.

BADGER

The best of fellows, of course. But young, young.

RAT

Y-yes. All the same, I don't see why . . . I mean, after all . . . I . . . well, I . . . Excuse me! (*And now he, too, is in the circle.*)

But others seem to have heard the news. The Jury come on, singing and dancing—

JURY

> There were calls from all the neighbors,
> there were letters from afar.

followed by the JUDGE *and the* USHER.

JUDGE

> There was groaning on the Bench.

USHER

> And there was moaning at the Bar.

Then PHOEBE—

PHOEBE

> There was tooting on the piccolo and
> fluting on the pipes.

and the WASHERWOMAN *and* BARGE-WOMAN.

WOMEN

> There was starching of 'is sockses and a
> washing of 'is wipes,

ALL

> When the Toad came home,
> When the Toad came home.

(*Enter* ALFRED.)

ALFRED

> There was shrieking in the gear-box, there
>> was trumpeting of horn,
> And the elephant was jealous and the
>> parrot felt forlorn.

ALL

> There were speeches from the gentry,
>> there was moistening of throats,

(*Enter* POLICEMAN.)

> And a moistening of pencils and a taking
>> down of notes.

ALL

> When the Toad came home,
> When the Toad came home.

(*Now they are all round* TOAD, *singing and dancing;
all but* BADGER.)

BADGER

Well, well, well. (*Doubtfully*) Well. (*Less doubtfully*)
W-w-well? (*His mind made up*) Oh, well! (*He joins the
dancers, and hobbles stiffly round with them.*)

ALL

> There was welcoming to Badger, when he
>> joined the merry throng.

BADGER

> I can do it for a little but I can't go on for
>> long. . . .

(*And so on. The incense of their adoration streams up to the be-laurelled* TOAD, *and with a long sigh of happiness he closes his eyes.*)

EPILOGUE

THE WIND IN THE WILLOWS

It is spring again. The wind is whispering in the willows that fringe the river. Faintly we hear its elfin music. Among her daffodils lies MARIGOLD, *in tumbled sleep. The dead leaves in the hollow rise and fall; they fall apart as an old gray* BADGER *heaves himself into the sunlight. Curiously he sniffs at* MARIGOLD, *and then lumbers away. A* WATER-RAT *twinkles out of his hole in the bank; a* MOLE *laboriously takes the air; they, too, pass the time of day with* MARIGOLD *before following in the wake of the* BADGER. *Last of all comes a* TOAD. "*Ah, Marigold, Marigold!*" *and so, waddling jauntily, after the others . . .*

But NURSE *is getting impatient. From afar her voice comes to us.*

NURSE
Marigold! Marigold! It's time we went, dear.

(MARIGOLD *sighs gently, and stirs a little in her sleep.*)

ABOUT A. A. MILNE

Alan Alexander Milne was born in London in 1882. At Trinity College, Cambridge, he was editor of the undergraduate paper, and later he became a free-lance journalist in London. In 1906 he was appointed assistant editor of *Punch*, but after serving in World War I he returned to his own writing. He enjoyed a distinguished career as a playwright, novelist and essayist until his death in 1956. A. A. Milne married the former Dorothy de Selincourt, also a writer, and they had one son.

The son, Christopher Robin Milne, inspired the delightful fantasies about a small boy and an endearing teddy bear which made the name of A. A. Milne famous throughout the world. The first book *When We Were Very Young* was published in 1924 and was followed by *Now We Are Six*, *Winnie The Pooh* and *The House at Pooh Corner*.

Toad of Toad Hall, written in 1929, brought together two eminent figures in the world of children's literature. The play's success in London, where it was one of the biggest hits of the Christmas season two years in a row, pleased Mr. Grahame. It is a tribute to A. A. Milne's understanding and skill that his dramatic composition so truly captured the essence of a book already considered a classic.

ABOUT KENNETH GRAHAME

Kenneth Grahame was born in Edinburgh in 1859. He was by profession a London banker and regarded his writing as an avocation. However, it was one he pursued with dedication. His first story appeared in the late 1880's and he was a contributor to the famous *Yellow Book*. In 1895 he published *The Golden Age* and in 1898 *Dream Days*, both books containing stories based on his own orphaned childhood. He married Elspeth Thomson in 1899.

Kenneth Grahame's greatest work, *The Wind in The Willows*, began as a series of stories created for his young son Alistair. The book was published in England and the United States in 1908. That same year illness forced Mr. Grahame to resign his post as Secretary of the Bank of England. He retired to his country home at Pangbourne where he lived quietly until his death in 1932.

Kenneth Grahame has been called a "gentle genius" who was more at home in the world of nature than in society. In 1931 he entertained Ernest H. Shepard before the artist executed his now-famed drawings for *The Wind in The Willows*. The author's only request of Mr. Shepard was a simple one, but it clearly revealed the depth of his feeling. "I love these little people," he said. "Be kind to them."